"Handbook of Advanced Mathematics"

SIMONE MALACRIDA

ANALYTICAL INDEX

Analytical index

INTRODUCTION

In this book we will provide all the foundations of advanced mathematics, including both the great discipline of mathematical analysis and all the disparate fields that have arisen over the last two centuries, including, to mention only a few of them, geometry differential and fractal, non-Euclidean geometries, algebraic topology, functional analysis, statistics, numerical analysis and mathematical logic.

Almost all of these notions were developed after the introduction of the formalism of mathematical analysis at the end of the seventeenth century and, since then, the path of mathematics has always continued in parallel between this sector and all the other possible sub-disciplines that gradually side by side and have taken independent paths.

To fully understand what is presented in the manual, knowledge and prerequisites of elementary mathematics are necessary, which we will not report here, such as for example everything connected to trigonometry, analytic geometry, matrix mathematics, complex numbers and the main functions elementary of real variable.

All this knowledge is present in the previously published *"Elementary mathematics manual"* which is to be considered as preparatory to what will be explained below and which represents a kind of first volume of the entire mathematical knowledge for which this manual is instead the completion given by the second part.

On the importance of mathematics in today's society and on the various meanings of mathematics as an artificial and universal language that describes Nature, please refer, therefore, to the introduction of the aforementioned previous manual.

It remains to understand why mathematical analysis has introduced that watershed between elementary and advanced mathematics.

There are two areas that complement each other in this discourse.

On the one hand, only with the introduction of mathematical analysis has it been possible to describe, with a suitable formalism, the equations that govern natural phenomena, be they physical, chemical or of other extraction, for example social or economic. In other words, mathematical analysis is the main tool for building those mechanisms

1

Introduction

that allow us to predict results, to design technologies and to think about new improvements to introduce.

On the other hand, mathematical analysis possesses, within its very nature, a specific peculiarity which clearly distinguishes it from the previous elementary mathematics. This will be evident from the first chapter of this handbook, for now we limit ourselves to saying how mathematical analysis provides for local considerations, not exclusively punctual. Just the passage from punctuality to locality will allow to build a discourse of globality, going far beyond the previous knowable.

This manual does not claim to present all the possible facets of every single sector of advanced mathematics or even to expose the demonstrations of the infinite theorems that dot the mathematical analysis and other related disciplines. First of all it is not in the scope of the writing and then an exorbitant amount of pages would be necessary, which contrasts with the spirit of a manual, by its nature synthetic and compendium.

In this handbook two major themes will be taken up several times, to underline their mutual importance.

The first is given by advanced geometry, in all its forms, precisely to indicate the parallel path between mathematics and geometry that has been present since the dawn of history.

The second argument is typical of the leap introduced by mathematical analysis and is related to topology which, for reasons of understanding, we will present in several parts of the manual.

At the end of the book, topics of general interest which can disregard mathematical analysis, such as advanced algebra, statistics and numerical analysis, will be presented.

The last chapter will be devoted to advanced mathematical logic. On closer inspection, the first chapter of the aforementioned *"Manual of elementary mathematics"* was dedicated to elementary logic. Closing this manual of advanced mathematics, again with logic, is by no means a coincidence: the development of mathematics is internal to logical constructs that give the compass of reference to all human reasoning.

Each individual chapter can be considered as a complete field of mathematics in itself, but only by analyzing all the topics will it be possible to touch the vastness of mathematics and that is why the order of the chapters reflects a succession of knowledge in continuous progress.

I – GENERAL TOPOLOGY

The conceptual leap between elementary and advanced mathematics was evident only after the introduction of mathematical analysis. The fact that this discipline was local, and not punctual, led to the study and development of topology, understood as the study of places and spaces not only in a geometric sense, but in a much broader sense. The general topology gives the foundations of all the underlying sectors, among which we can include the algebraic topology, the differential one, the advanced one and so on.

We define topology as a collection T of subsets of a general set X for which the following three properties hold:

1) The empty set and the general set X belong to the collection T.
2) The union of an arbitrary quantity of sets belonging to T belongs to T.
3) The intersection of a finite number of sets belonging to T belongs to T.

A topological space is defined with a pair (X, T) and the sets constituting the collection T are open sets. Particular topologies can be the trivial one in which T is formed by X and the empty set and the discrete one in which T coincides with the set of parts of X. In the first topology only the empty set and X are open sets, while in the discrete one all sets are open sets. Two topologies are comparable if one of them is a subset of the other, while if one topology contains the other, the first is said to be finer than the second. The set of all topologies is partially ordered: the trivial topology is the least fine, the discrete is the finest, and all other possible topologies have intermediate fineness between these two.

In a topological space, a set I containing a point x belonging to X is called (open) neighborhood of x if there exists an open set A contained in I containing x:

$$x \in A \subseteq I$$

A subset of a topological space is closed if its complement is open. Closed sets have three properties:

I – General topology

1) The union of a finite number of closed sets is a closed set.
2) The intersection of closed sets is a closed set.
3) The set X and the empty set are closed.

With these properties, a topology based on closed sets can be constructed. In general, a subset can be closed, open, both open and closed, neither open nor closed.

Said S a subset of a topological space X, x is a point of closure of S if every neighborhood (open or closed) of x contains at least one point of S.

Said S a subset of a topological space X, x is an accumulation point of S if every neighborhood (open or closed) of x contains at least one point of S different from x itself.

Each accumulation point is a closing point while vice versa is not valid. Locking points that are not accumulation points are called isolated points.

The set of all closure points of a given set is called closure and is denoted by cl(I). The closure in a set is a closed set and contains the starting set, moreover it is the intersection of all closed sets that contain the starting set and is the smallest closed set containing the starting set. These definitions go by the name of topological closure.

A set is therefore closed if and only if it coincides with its own closure.

Finally, the closure of a subset is a subset of the closure of the main set, and a closed set contains another set if and only if this set contains the closure of the second.

It goes without saying that the closure of the empty set is the empty set, that of the general set X is the general set X and in a discrete space each set is equal to its closure.

Said S a subset of a topological space X, x is an interior point of S if there exists a neighborhood (open or closed) of x contained in S.

The set of all interior points of a given set is called the interior and is denoted by int(I). The inner part is an open subset of the starting set, it is the union of all open sets contained in that set and it is the largest open set contained in that set. These definitions are referred to as the topological interior.

A set is open if and only it coincides with its interior, furthermore the interior satisfies the idempotence relation.

Finally, the interior of a subset is a subset of the interior of the main set, and an open set contains another set if and only if that set contains the interior of the second.

I – General topology

It goes without saying that the interior of the empty set is the empty set, that of the general set X is the general set X and in a discrete space each set is equal to its interior.

A closed subset of a topological space is said to be rare if it has no interior. A topological space is said to be of the first category if it is the union of a countable family of rare closed sets, vice versa it is said to be of the second category.

The internal part and the closure can be associated with operators that put these two concepts into a dual relationship.

The set difference between the closure and the interior is called the frontier, an element belonging to the frontier is called the frontier point. The frontier is also the intersection between the closure and its complement and is defined as the set of points such that each neighborhood contains at least one point belonging to the set and at least one point not belonging to this set.

The boundary of a set is closed. A set is closed if and only if its boundary is contained in the set while it is open if and only if its boundary is disjoint from it.

The frontier of a set is equal to the frontier of its complement, and the closing operation is simply the union of the set with its frontier. The boundary of a set is empty if and only if the set is both closed and open.

A subset of a topological space is locally closed if it satisfies at least one of the following conditions: it is open in its closure or it is open in any closed space or it is closed in any open space or if for each point of the subset there is an open neighborhood of this point such that the intersection between the neighborhood and the subset is closed in the neighborhood.

A topological space is said to be compact if from any family of open subsets of the space whose cover is given by:

$$\bigcup_{i \in I} U_i \supseteq X$$

one can extract a finite subset J in I such that the same covering relation holds. This is the so-called covering compactness and can also be defined by the use of closed sets.

A topological space is said to be compact by sequences if every sequence of points in the space admits a sub-sequence converging to a point in the space.

I – General topology

The Bolzano-Weierstrass theorem states that every infinite subset of a compact space admits at least one accumulation point.

A closed subset of a compact is a compact; the product of compact spaces is a compact as is the quotient.

The empty set and any set defined with the trivial topology are compact. A closed and bounded interval in the set of real numbers is compact. Every finite topological space is also compact, as is the closed sphere in RxR and the Cantor set (which we will discuss at length in the chapter dedicated to fractal geometry, almost at the end of the book). Infinite sets with discrete topology are not compact.

A space is said to be locally compact which, for each point, admits a basis of neighborhoods made up of compact sets.

A non-empty topological space is said to be connected if the only pair of disjoint subsets whose union is the space itself is given by the pair between the space and the empty set. Equivalently we can state that a topological space is connected if and only if the only subsets both open and closed are the empty set and the space itself.

A connected component of a space is called a connected subset not contained in any other connected subset. A space whose connected components are its points is said to be totally disconnected. The Cantor set and a set with discrete topology are totally disconnected.

The union of lines in the plane is a connected space if at least two lines are not parallel, while in the set of real numbers a subset is connected if and only if it is an interval in which each extreme can be infinite. Furthermore, the product of connected spaces is a connected space.

A topological space is said to be connected by arcs, or by paths, if for each pair of points in the space there is a continuous function (for the definition of continuity, see the next chapter) which connects them with equal value to the endpoints of the path. Every space connected by paths is connected, but not vice versa.

A space is locally connected if it has a system of connected neighborhoods. A path-connected topological space is simply connected if the path is contractible at will up to the transformation (called homotopy) in the constant path.

We define continuous function between topological spaces as a function for which the counterimage of every open set is open.

We define Hausdorff space as a topological space which satisfies the following axioms:

1) At least one neighborhood of the point containing the point itself corresponds to each point in space.

2) Given two neighborhoods of the same point, the intersection of these two neighborhoods is a neighborhood.
3) If a neighborhood of a point is a subset of a set, then this set is also a neighborhood of the point.
4) For each neighborhood of a point there exists another neighborhood of that point such that the first neighborhood is the neighborhood of any point belonging to the second neighborhood.
5) Given two distinct points there are two disjoint neighbourhoods.

In particular, the last axiom is called the Hausdorff separability axiom of topological spaces. The separability axioms of topological spaces can be generalized according to a category of successive refinements:

1) Spaces T_0: for each pair of points there is an open space which contains one point and not the other.
2) Spaces T_1: for each pair of points there are two open spaces such that both contain one of the two points but not the other.
3) Spaces T_2: for each pair of points there are two open disjoints which contain them respectively. These are Hausdorff spaces.
4) Regular spaces: for each point and for each closed disjoint there exist two open disjoints which contain them respectively.
5) Spaces T_3: if they are T_2 and regular.
6) Completely regular spaces: for every disjoint point and for every closed set there exists a continuous function with real values which is 0 in the closed set and 1 in the point.
7) Spaces $T_{3\frac{1}{2}}$: if they are T_3 and completely regular.

8) Normal spaces: for each pair of closed disjoints there are two open disjoints which contain them respectively.
9) Spaces T_4: if they are T_3 and normal.

Open or closed subsets of a locally compact Hausdorff space are locally compact. Any compact Hausdorff space is second rate.
We recall that in topological spaces notions of elementary mathematics such as the concepts of countability or cardinality can be extended, thus defining countable sets and continuous sets.
A subset is dense in a topological space if every element of the subset belongs to the set or is accumulation point. Equivalent definitions are the following: a subset is dense if its closure is the topological space or

I – General topology

if every non-empty open subset intersects the subset or if the complement of the subset has an empty interior or if each point of the space is the limit of a sequence contained in the subset.

Every topological space is dense in itself; rational and irrational numbers are dense in the set of real numbers. A space is separable if its dense subset is countable. A set is never dense if it is not dense in any open set.

A topological space is uniform if it has a family of subsets satisfying the following properties:

1) Every family of subsets contains the diagonal of the Cartesian product X x X.
2) Every family of subsets is closed under inclusion.
3) Every family of subsets is closed under the intersection.
4) If a neighborhood belongs to the topology then there exists a family of subsets belonging to the topology such that, if two pairs of points having a common point belong to the family of subsets, then the two disjoint points belong to the neighborhood.
5) If a neighborhood belongs to the topology then also the inversion of the neighborhood in the Cartesian product belongs to the topology.

A metric space is a topological space generated by a topology of a basis of circular neighborhoods. In metric spaces a metric is defined which associates a non-negative real number to two points in the space for which the following properties hold:

$$d(x, y) > 0 \Leftrightarrow x \neq y$$
$$d(x, y) = 0 \Leftrightarrow x = y$$
$$d(x, y) = d(y, x)$$
$$d(x, y) \leq d(x, z) + d(z, y)$$

A function is said to be continuous at a point on a metric space if, for any choice of arbitrary positive quantities, the distance between this point and another point is bounded. Considering the spherical neighborhoods and the domain of the function we have:

$$\forall \varepsilon > 0, \exists \delta > 0 : f(D \cap B_\delta(p)) \subset B_\varepsilon(f(p))$$

I – General topology

A metric space is always uniform. In a metric space, the distance between a point and a set also holds, defined as:

$$\delta(x, I) = \inf_{y \in I} d(x, y)$$

This distance is zero if and only if x belongs to the closure of I. The distance between two points of two sets can be defined in the same way. Instead, it dictates the excess of one set over the other:

$$e(A, B) = \sup_{x \in A} \delta(a, B)$$

The Hausdorff distance is as follows:

$$H(A, B) = \max\{e(A, B), e(B, A)\}$$

A metric space is bounded if its closure is bounded. In a metric space x is a closure point if for every positive radius there exists a point within the space such that the distance between x and this point is less than the radius. In a metric space x is an interior point if there exists a positive radius such that the distance between x and a generic point belonging to the space is smaller than the radius.
A metric space is complete if every Cauchy sequence converges to an element of the space. A metric space is compact if and only if it is complete and totally bounded. A metric space is always dense in its completion.
We define a normed space as a metric space in which the distance is expressed by the norm:

$$d(x, y) = \|x - y\|$$

The norm has the properties of being positive definite and homogeneous; moreover, the triangle inequality holds. In formulas we have:

$$\|x\| \geq 0 \,|\, \|x\| = 0 \Leftrightarrow x = 0$$
$$\forall \lambda \in C : \|\lambda x\| = |\lambda| \|x\|$$

$$\|x + y\| \le \|x\| + \|y\|$$

A metric space in which the first relation does not hold is said to be semi-normed. It goes without saying that every regulated space is a metric (and therefore topological) space. An infinite-dimensional normed space is not locally compact.

A metric space in which the distance (and therefore the norm) are Euclidean is called Euclidean space. This space is the usual one of elementary geometry, in fact the n-dimensional distance is very reminiscent of the classic Pythagorean theorem:

$$d(x,y) = \|x - y\| = \sqrt{\sum_{i=1}^{n}(x_i - y_i)^2}$$

Defined as a subset of an n-dimensional Euclidean space, a point x is closure if every open n-dimensional sphere centered on x contains at least one point of the subset. Similarly, a point x is interior if there is an open n-dimensional sphere centered at the point and contained in the subset.

Euclidean spaces are locally compact. The n-dimensional sphere, the line, the plane and any Euclidean space are simply connected. The Euclidean space consisting of the set of n-dimensional real numbers is a connected space. By the Heine-Borel theorem a subset of this Euclidean space is compact if and only if it is closed.

In a Euclidean space a convex set is a set in which, for each pair of points, the path connecting them is entirely contained in the set. A convex set is simply connected.

A homeomorphism between two topological spaces is a continuous, bijective function with continuous inverse. The homeomorphism relation between topological spaces is an equivalence relation. Two homeomorphic spaces have the same topological properties. Local homeomorphism occurs if the function is locally but not globally continuous. Every local homeomorphism is a continuous and open function, every bijective local homeomorphism is a homeomorphism, the composition of two local homeomorphisms is another local homeomorphism.

A diffeomorphism is a function between two topological spaces with the property of being differentiable (see below for the definition of differentiability), invertible and with differentiable inverse. The diffeomorphism is local if the function has these properties locally but not globally. A local diffeomorphism is a particular kind of local homeomorphism, so it is open.

An isomorphism is a bijective map such that both the function and its inverse are homeomorphisms. The structures are said to be isomorphic and are substantially identical. If there is also an ordering property, we speak of order isomorphism or isotonia.

A homotopy between two continuous functions defined in two topological spaces is a continuous function between the Cartesian product of a topological space and the unit interval [0,1] which associates to the zero point the value of the first continuous function and to the one point the value of the second continuous function. Homotopy is an equivalence relation, every homeomorphism is an equivalence of homotopy. Two homotopic topological spaces maintain the properties of path connection and simple connection.

A bijective function between two metric spaces is called isometry if it holds

$$d_2(f(x), f(y)) = d_1(x, y)$$

If this relation is multiplicative for an arbitrary positive number other than one, it is called similarity. Furthermore, it is called uniformity if it is an isomorphism between uniform Euclidean spaces and it is a homeomorphism if it is an isomorphism between two topological spaces.

An n-dimensional topological manifold is a topological Hausdorff space in which every point has an open neighborhood which is homeomorphic to an open set in n-dimensional Euclidean space. The number n is called the dimension of the manifold. The topological manifolds of dimension one are the circle and the straight line, those of dimensions two are called surfaces (examples are the sphere, the torus, the Mobius strip, the Klein bottle). For three-dimensional topological manifolds the Poincaré conjecture holds true (which states that every three-dimensional topological manifold that is simply connected and closed is homeomorphic to a three-dimensional sphere), those of four dimension represent the space-time of general relativity. Topological manifolds are homeomorphic to Euclidean spaces and hence are locally compact.

A topological subspace is a subset of a topological space that inherits the topological structure of the space.

I – General topology

We refer to the following chapters for insights into advanced, algebraic, functional and vector topology. This first introduction to general topology was necessary to fully understand the innovations introduced by mathematical analysis, which we will discuss shortly.

II - LIMITS AND CONTINUITY

Mathematical analysis is that part of mathematics that deals with the infinite decomposition of dense objects or sets, therefore it is based on topological concepts expressed in the first chapter.

In particular, it involves two complementary and antithetical concepts, those of infinitesimal and infinite.

Starting from the topological definition of neighborhood, an infinitesimal is any small quantity, but always different from zero. This shifts the attention from a punctual vision, typical of elementary mathematics, to a local vision, which instead characterizes mathematical analysis, closely connected to the general topology.

The discussion of the infinite starts instead from the removal of the condition of existence typical of real numbers, according to which the denominator of a fraction must always be different from zero. In mathematical analysis, a number divided by zero results in infinity, whose symbol is as follows ∞. If the signs agree, infinity is positive, if they disagree, it is negative. It should be noted that infinities (and infinitesimals) are not all the same, as we will soon see.

The introduction of mathematical analysis was made in the second half of the seventeenth century, by Newton and Leibnitz, and immediately had great physical and engineering applications. On the other hand, it was precisely mathematical analysis that allowed the overcoming of ancient questions, such as that of Zeno's paradox.

As far as we will say, and barring explicit exceptions, all the concepts expressed hereafter are valid only for separable topological spaces, in particular for Hausdorff spaces.

Given a function defined on a subset X of the set of real numbers and a point of accumulation of this subset, we define the limit of the function as x tending to the point of accumulation a real number such that the distance between it and the value of the function at the point is an infinitesimal. In formulas:

$$\forall \varepsilon > 0, \exists \delta > 0, \forall x \in X \subseteq R : \left| f(x) - l \right| < \varepsilon \Leftrightarrow 0 < \left| x - x_0 \right| < \delta$$

In this case we say that the limit as x tending to the point of accumulation of the function is given by l.

13

$$\lim_{x \to x_0} f(x) = l$$

Equivalently we can say that for every neighborhood of l there exists a neighborhood of the accumulation point such that the function belongs to the neighborhood of l.

$$f : X \to R, \forall U(l) \in R, \exists V(x_0) \in R, \forall x \neq x_0 \in V \cap X : f(x) \in U(l)$$

We point out that the point of accumulation is not necessarily contained in the domain of the function, i.e. the local vision is totally independent of the punctual one.

We can extend the concept of limit if the real number l is infinite. In this case it is valid:

$$\forall N > 0, \exists \delta > 0, \forall x \in X \subseteq R : f(x) > N \Leftrightarrow 0 < |x - x_0| < \delta$$

The limit is written like this:

$$\lim_{x \to x_0} f(x) = +\infty$$

A further extension is given by the condition in which the point of accumulation is at infinity, ie that the upper bound of the set X is infinite. In that case:

$$\forall \varepsilon > 0, \exists S > 0, \forall x \in X \subseteq R : |f(x) - l| < \varepsilon \Leftrightarrow x > S$$

Which leads to this definition of limit:

$$\lim_{x \to +\infty} f(x) = l$$

Obviously analogous cases are valid for the negative signs of infinity and the two extensions can be combined for accumulation points at infinity and limit with infinite value.

If we consider the extended real set, ie the set of real numbers with the addition of infinities of both signs, all these concepts can be unified. The extended real set is ordered and is a topological space, having

14

II – Limits and continuity

defined the neighborhoods of infinity as those sets which contain any half-line. With these premises, the following unifying notation of limit holds:

$$f : X \to R^*, \forall U(l) \in R^*, \exists V(x_0) \in R^*, \forall x \neq x_0 \in V \cap X : f(x) \in U(l)$$

If the limit of a function is finite, the function is said to converge at the point of accumulation. If the limit is infinite, the function is said to diverge.

We define the right limit as the limit of the function in the right neighborhood of the accumulation point, the same is done for the left one and are indicated as follows:

$$\lim_{x \to x_0^+} f(x)$$

$$\lim_{x \to x_0^-} f(x)$$

The respective limit values are said by excess and by default and are indicated with the plus or minus sign in superscript.

Given two functions defined on non-disjoint domains and an accumulation point belonging to the intersection of the two domains, if the limits of the two functions exist and are finite, the following operations can be performed:

$$c \cdot \lim_{x \to x_0} f(x) = \lim_{x \to x_0} c \cdot f(x) = c \cdot l_1$$

$$\lim_{x \to x_0}[f(x) \pm g(x)] = \lim_{x \to x_0} f(x) \pm \lim_{x \to x_0} g(x) = l_1 \pm l_2$$

$$\lim_{x \to x_0}[f(x) \cdot g(x)] = \lim_{x \to x_0} f(x) \cdot \lim_{x \to x_0} g(x) = l_1 \cdot l_2$$

$$\lim_{x \to x_0}\left[\frac{f(x)}{g(x)}\right] = \frac{\lim_{x \to x_0} f(x)}{\lim_{x \to x_0} g(x)} = \frac{l_1}{l_2} \Leftrightarrow l_2 \neq 0$$

If one of the two limits is infinite, the following hold instead:

$$f(x) \to \pm\infty, c > 0 \Rightarrow c \cdot \lim_{x \to x_0} f(x) = \lim_{x \to x_0} c \cdot f(x) = \pm\infty$$

$$f(x) \to \pm\infty \Rightarrow \lim_{x \to x_0}[f(x) \pm g(x)] = \lim_{x \to x_0} f(x) \pm \lim_{x \to x_0} g(x) = \pm\infty$$

15

$$f(x) \to \pm\infty \Rightarrow \lim_{x \to x_0} \frac{1}{f(x)} = 0^{\pm}$$

$$f(x) \to 0^{\pm} \Rightarrow \lim_{x \to x_0} \frac{1}{f(x)} = \pm\infty$$

$$f(x) \to \pm\infty, l > 0 \Rightarrow \lim_{x \to x_0}[f(x) \cdot g(x)] = \lim_{x \to x_0} f(x) \cdot \lim_{x \to x_0} g(x) = \pm\infty$$

The limit operation is therefore characterized as a functional, ie as an application between a space of functions and a numerical set. This functional is linear and continuous.

Some operations on limits return forms of indeterminacy that we will study shortly.

The uniqueness theorem of the limit states that a function defined on an open set of the set of real numbers cannot have two distinct limits in a point of accumulation so the limit, if it exists, is unique.

The local boundedness theorem states that a function whose limit is finite at an accumulation point is bounded around that point.

For two functions defined in an open domain of the set of real numbers, the property holds that if one function is greater than the other in the neighborhood of an accumulation point, then also the limit of the first function is greater than the other.

From this assumption we can enunciate the comparison theorem, ie that a function between two others has the same limit as the first two if they converge to an identical limit.

The following notable limits are useful for solving the calculation of limits:

$$\lim_{x \to 0} \frac{(1+x)^a - 1}{x} = a$$

$$\lim_{x \to 0} \frac{\sin x}{x} = \lim_{x \to 0} \frac{\sinh x}{x} = \lim_{x \to 0} \frac{\tan x}{x} = \lim_{x \to 0} \frac{\arcsin x}{x} = \lim_{x \to 0} \frac{\arctan x}{x} = 1$$

$$\lim_{x \to 0} \frac{1 - \cos x}{x} = 0$$

$$\lim_{x \to \infty} \frac{\sin x}{x} = 0$$

$$\lim_{x \to 0} \frac{1 - \cos x}{x^2} = \lim_{x \to 0} \frac{\cosh x - 1}{x^2} = \frac{1}{2}$$

16

$$\lim_{x\to\infty}\left(1+\frac{1}{x}\right)^x = e$$

$$\lim_{x\to 0}(1+ax)^{\frac{1}{x}} = e^a$$

$$\lim_{x\to 0}\frac{a^x-1}{x} = \ln a$$

$$\lim_{x\to 0}\frac{e^x-1}{x} = 1$$

$$\lim_{x\to 0}\frac{\log_a(1+x)}{x} = \log_a e$$

$$\lim_{x\to 0}\frac{\ln(1+x)}{x} = 1$$

Some of these notable limits will be clarified when the series expansions of functions are introduced. For now we can see how this is reflected in the so-called asymptotic estimate.

The starting point of the asymptotic estimation is given by the assumption that the infinites are not all equal to each other and neither are the infinitesimals.

Given two polynomials, the one with greater degree has a more "powerful" infinity and therefore in a fraction it dominates over the other. By doing so, it can be seen that:

$$\lim_{x\to+\infty}\frac{p_1^m(x)}{p_2^n(x)} = \begin{cases}\infty \Leftrightarrow m>n \\ 0 \Leftrightarrow m<n \\ l=\dfrac{a_1}{a_2} \Leftrightarrow m=n\end{cases}$$

Where a are the numerical coefficients of the respective monomials of higher degree. In a completely opposite way we reason for the infinitesimals, i.e. an infinitesimal of higher order prevails over one of lower order, however overturning the behavior on the results.

II – Limits and continuity

Taking up concepts derived from sequences and introducing Landau symbols, we can define two functions and say that one is O-larger than the other if it happens that:

$$\exists c > 0, n_0 \in N : \forall n \geq n_0, |f(n)| \leq c|g(n)| \Leftrightarrow \lim_{n \to \infty} \sup \left| \frac{f(n)}{g(n)} \right| < \infty \Leftrightarrow f(n) = O(g(n))$$

Instead, it is defined as o-small if it occurs:

$$\lim_{n \to \infty} \left| \frac{f(n)}{g(n)} \right| = 0 \Leftrightarrow f(n) = o(g(n))$$

The analogous concepts relating to infinitesimals are called big omega and small omega. If instead it happens that the two sequences have the same order of magnitude, the theta expression is used:

$$\exists c_1, c_2 > 0, n_0 \in N : \forall n \geq n_0, c_1|g(n)| \leq f(n) \leq c_2|g(n)| \Leftrightarrow 0 < \lim_{n \to \infty} \inf \left| \frac{f(n)}{g(n)} \right| \leq \lim_{n \to \infty} \sup \left| \frac{f(n)}{g(n)} \right| < \infty$$

$$f(n) = \Theta(g(n))$$

Thanks to the asymptotic estimation it is possible to solve the so-called forms of indetermination which are the following: division between infinitesimals or between infinitesimals, multiplication of an infinitesimal by an infinitesimal, subtraction between infinitesimals, exponentiation of an infinitesimal to infinity (or vice versa) and exponentiation of one to infinity.

Alongside the polynomial functions, the transcendental functions are classified as follows: logarithmic infinity is less powerful than any polynomial function, whatever the degree of the polynomial, while exponential infinity is more powerful than any polynomial function. Trigonometric functions such as sine and cosine, being oscillating and bounded, do not have characteristics at infinity, so much so that their limit at infinity does not exist. In formulas:

$$\lim_{x \to \infty} \frac{\log_b x}{x^a} = 0 \Leftrightarrow \lim_{x \to 0^+} x^a \log_b x = 0$$

$$\lim_{x \to +\infty} \frac{x^a}{e^x} = 0 \Leftrightarrow \lim_{x \to -\infty} x^a e^x = 0$$

18

II – Limits and continuity

A function with real variable is said to be continuous at a point (of accumulation) if its limit as x tending to that point coincides with the value of the function at that point.

$$\lim_{x \to x_0} f(x) = f(x_0)$$

In this case, the local vision coincides with the punctual one, even if the information contained at the local level is of a higher order. A function is said to be continuous if it is continuous at every point in its domain. An analogous expression for continuous functions is given by making explicit the concept of limit:

$$\forall \varepsilon > 0, \exists \delta > 0, \forall x \in X \subseteq R : |x - x_0| < \delta \Leftrightarrow |f(x) - f(x_0)| < \varepsilon$$

Equivalently, topological concepts and neighborhoods can be used: a function between two topological spaces is continuous if the counterimage of every open set is open and it is continuous in a point if the counterimage of each neighborhood of the function is a neighborhood of the point.

In a metric space, a function is continuous if:

$$\forall \varepsilon > 0, \exists \delta > 0, \forall x \in X \subseteq R : d_1(x, x_0) < \delta \Leftrightarrow d_2(f(x), f(x_0)) < \varepsilon$$

The constants, the identity function, the polynomials, the rational, exponential, logarithmic functions are continuous functions. So are sine, cosine and linear transformations between Euclidean spaces.

A function is said to be inferiorly (or superiorly) semicontinuous if it is continuous only on the inferior (or superior) limit. The integer function is upper semicontinuous, the Dirichlet function (which is zero at every irrational point and one at every rational point) is lower semicontinuous at every irrational point, upper at every rational point.

A function is continuous if and only if it is both lower and upper semicontinuous. An inferior semicontinuous function in a compact set has a minimum, an upper semicontinuous function in a compact set has a maximum.

A function is said to be uniformly continuous if:

II – Limits and continuity

$$\forall \varepsilon > 0, \exists \delta > 0, \forall x_1, x_2 \in X \subseteq R : |x_1 - x_2| < \delta \Leftrightarrow |f(x_1) - f(x_2)| < \varepsilon$$

An equivalent definition can be given for topological and metric spaces. The constants, the identity function, the linear functions, sine and cosine are uniformly continuous functions, while polynomials with degree greater than one are not.

The Heine-Cantor theorem states that continuous functions on a compact set are uniformly continuous. It goes without saying that uniformly continuous functions are continuous.

The set of all continuous functions on a fixed real-valued domain represents a vector space, denoted by $C^0(R)$.

The composition of continuous functions is a continuous function just as the sum, the difference, the product and the quotient of two continuous functions are continuous functions, while the converse is not necessarily true.

Furthermore, if the function is bijective and the set is compact, the inverse function is also continuous.

If the function is continuous between topological spaces, the counterimage of an open (or closed) set is an open (or closed) set, while the image of a compact (or connected) set is a compact (or connected) set.

For continuous functions some fundamental theorems also hold.

The sign permanence theorem states that if the function is positive at a given point within its domain, then there exists a neighborhood of that point such that the function is positive at all points in the neighborhood.

The intermediate value theorem states that the function takes on all values between the value at one point in the domain and the value at another point in the domain.

Bolzano's theorem (or existence of zeros) states that given two points of the domain in which the function assumes discordant values, then there exists at least one point of the domain between the two previous points such that the function assumes a null value.

Weierstrass's theorem states that if the interval is closed and bounded, then the function has a maximum and a minimum in the interval (or it is a constant). This theorem extends to metric spaces in the case of compact sets.

A function that is not continuous at a point is said to have a point of discontinuity. Breakpoints are divided into three distinct species:

II – Limits and continuity

1) Discontinuity of the first kind: the right limit and the left limit exist and are finite, but they are different from each other.

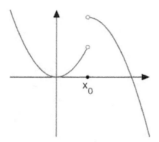

2) Discontinuity of the second kind: at least one of the two limits between the right and the left are infinite or do not exist.

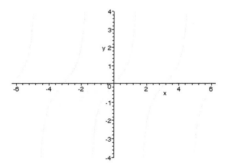

3) Discontinuity of the third kind: the right limit and the left limit exist, they are finite and equal to each other, but different from the value of the function at the point.

A function which has a discontinuity of the first kind is, for example, the sign function which has a point of discontinuity at zero.
The discontinuity points of the second kind occur when the function is evaluated in a neighborhood of an accumulation point which however does not belong to the domain of the function.
A discontinuity of the third kind is also said to be eliminated because it can be removed simply by redefining the value of that function at the point.
The Dirichlet function is discontinuous at every point, every point being a discontinuity of the first kind.

21

II – Limits and continuity

III – DIFFERENTIAL CALCULATION

Given a real function of real variable, we call the increment of the function around a given point, the following quantity:

$$\Delta f(x_0) := f(x_0 + h) - f(x_0)$$

While the increment of the independent variable is given by h. The incremental ratio is defined as the ratio of the increments:

$$\frac{\Delta f}{\Delta x} = \frac{f(x_0 + h) - f(x_0)}{h}$$

If h is positive, we speak of right incremental ratio, if it is negative, of left incremental ratio.

The limit as h tends to zero of the incremental ratio is called the derivative and is indicated in various ways.

$$\lim_{h \to 0} \frac{f(x_0 + h) - f(x_0)}{h} = f'(x_0) = \left(\frac{df}{dx}\right)_{x_0} = D[f(x_0)] = \frac{df(x_0)}{dx} = \dot{f}(x_0)$$

The first notation is that of Lagrange, the second is used in physics, the third is the notation of Cauchy-Euler, the fourth is that of Leibnitz, the last is that of Newton.

The derivative calculated in the right neighborhood is called the right derivative and the one calculated in the left neighborhood is called the left derivative. A function is differentiable at a point if and only if there are finite left and right limits of the incremental ratio and these limits are equal. A function is differentiable everywhere, or in an interval, if it is differentiable at any point, or at any point in the interval.

The function which assumes at each point the value of the derivative at that point is called a derivative function, precisely because it derives from the starting function.

The derivative of the derivative is called the second derivative and so on up to the n-th derivative which is indicated as follows:

III – Differential calculus

$$f^n(x) = \left(\frac{d^n f}{dx^n}\right) = D^n[f(x)]$$

Having used the previous notations to indicate the nth derivative.
A necessary condition for the derivability of a function is its continuity.
Continuous and differentiable functions (therefore with continuous first derivative) are part of a vector space denoted by $C^1(R)$, while a function with continuous n-th derivative is part of the space $C^n(R)$ and a function having infinite continuous derivatives is part of the space $C^\infty(R)$ (these functions are called harmonics or smooth). It goes without saying that the following relationship holds:

$$C^\infty(R) \subset C^n(R) \subset ... \subset C^1(R) \subset C^0(R)$$

In essence they are all vector subspaces of the more general vector space.
When calculating derivatives, the following rules apply:

$$[af(x) \pm bg(x)]' = af'(x) \pm bg'(x)$$

$$[f(x) \cdot g(x)]' = f'(x) \cdot g(x) + f(x) \cdot g'(x)$$

$$\left[\frac{f(x)}{g(x)}\right]' = \frac{f'(x) \cdot g(x) - f(x) \cdot g'(x)}{[g(x)]^2}$$

$$\left[\frac{1}{f(x)}\right]' = -\frac{f'(x)}{[f(x)]^2}$$

$$[f^{-1}(y)]' = \frac{1}{f'(x)}$$

$$[f(g(x))]' = f'(g(x)) \cdot g'(x)$$

The basic derivatives are the following:

$$D(k) = 0$$

$$D(x^n) = nx^{n-1}$$

24

$$D(a^x) = a^x \ln a$$
$$D(e^x) = e^x$$
$$D(\log_b x) = \frac{1}{x \ln b}$$
$$D(\ln x) = \frac{1}{x}$$
$$D(\sin x) = \cos x$$
$$D(\cos x) = -\sin x$$
$$D(\tan x) = \frac{1}{\cos^2 x}$$
$$D(\cot x) = -\frac{1}{\sin^2 x}$$
$$D(\sec x) = \tan x \sec x$$
$$D(\csc x) = -\cot x \csc x$$
$$D(\arcsin x) = \frac{1}{\sqrt{1-x^2}}$$
$$D(\arccos x) = -\frac{1}{\sqrt{1-x^2}}$$
$$D(\arctan x) = \frac{1}{1+x^2}$$
$$D(\text{arc} \cot x) = -\frac{1}{1+x^2}$$
$$D(\sinh x) = \cosh x$$
$$D(\cosh x) = \sinh x$$
$$D(\tanh x) = \frac{1}{\cosh^2 x}$$
$$D(\coth x) = -\frac{1}{\sinh^2 x}$$

The exponential, sine, cosine, tangent, and cotangent functions are harmonic functions.
The prime differential of a function is given by:

25

III – Differential calculus

$$df(x) = f'(x)dx$$

The successive differentials are calculated in the same way considering the successive derivatives.

Fermat's theorem on stationary points states that a continuous and derivable function at an accumulation point of an open domain has zero derivative if the point is stationary.

Rolle's theorem states that a continuous function in a closed interval and differentiable in the same interval, but open, having equal values at the ends admits at least one point inside the interval in which the derivative vanishes (therefore admits at least one stationary point).

Lagrange's theorem states that a continuous function in a closed interval and differentiable in the same interval, but open, admits at least one point inside this interval in which the following relation holds:

$$f'(x_0) = \frac{f(b) - f(a)}{b - a}$$

Where a and b are the boundary points of the interval.

Cauchy's theorem states that two continuous functions in a closed interval and differentiable in the same but open interval admit at least one point inside this interval in which the following relation holds:

$$\frac{f'(x_0)}{g'(x_0)} = \frac{f(b) - f(a)}{g(b) - g(a)}$$

Where the function g(x) has different values at the extremes and derivative always different from zero within the considered interval.

From these theorems derives the theorem of the constant function which states that a continuous function in a closed interval and differentiable in the same interval, but open, is a constant if and only if its derivative is zero everywhere in its interval.

Furthermore, the sign of the first derivative of a function is strictly connected to its monotonicity. A continuous function in a closed interval and differentiable in the same interval, but open, with always positive derivative within this interval means that it is always increasing in this interval. If, on the other hand, the derivative is always negative, it means that it is always decreasing.

III – Differential calculus

The sign of the second derivative is instead related to the convexity of the function. A continuous function in a closed interval and derivable in the same interval, but open, having a definite second derivative is convex if and only if its second derivative is always positive. If its second derivative is always negative, it is concave.

As we will see, the properties of the derivatives will be fundamental for the study of functions of real variables, in particular for determining the stationary points of the first derivative (maximum, minimum or inflection with horizontal tangent) and of the second derivative (inflection with oblique tangent). Differential calculus, in addition to being useful for the study of functions, provides a rule, called Hopital's, for the resolution of some forms of indeterminacy of limits. Given two continuous functions in a closed interval and differentiable in the same interval, but open, in the case in which there is a form of indeterminacy of the type zero divided by zero or infinity divided by infinity, the following rule holds:

$$\lim_{x \to x_0} \frac{f'(x)}{g'(x)} = \lim_{x \to x_0} \frac{f(x)}{g(x)} = l$$

Where obviously the denominators are well defined in the range, except at the maximum at the point of accumulation. In essence, this theorem allows us to solve the forms of indeterminacy by applying the derivative to the numerator and denominator until we obtain a finite limit. This theorem can be applied iteratively for successive derivatives. The derivative in a point also has a remarkable geometric meaning which allows us to connect this concept with those of elementary analytic geometry. The derivative at a point is the angular coefficient of the tangent line at the point, in other words we have this unifying relation:

$$m = \tan \alpha = f'(x_0)$$

III – Differential calculus

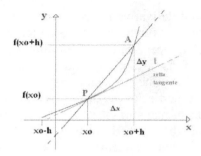

Furthermore, the derivative also has a powerful physical meaning. In fact, every physical quantity that can be expressed through a ratio is the derivative of the function in the numerator in relation to the denominator. For example, velocity is the first derivative of space with respect to time, acceleration the first derivative of velocity with respect to time, and so on for all the almost infinite physical quantities definable in this way.

IV – INTEGRAL CALCULATION

Considering a continuous function in a closed and bounded interval [a,b], one can define two points within any partition of the interval given by the lower bound and the upper bound as follows:

$$m_k = \inf_{x\in[x_{k-1},x_k]} f(x)$$
$$M_k = \sup_{x\in[x_{k-1},x_k]} f(x)$$

The lower and upper integral sums are constructed as follows:

$$s(P) = \sum_{k=1}^{n} m_k (x_k - x_{k-1})$$
$$S(P) = \sum_{k=1}^{n} M_k (x_k - x_{k-1})$$

We define the following quantity as an integral sum:

$$\sigma_n = \frac{b-a}{n} \sum_{k=1}^{n} f(x_k - x_{k-1})$$

The limit of this integral sum (if it exists finitely) is called the Riemann integral and is indicated as follows:

$$\int_a^b f(x)dx = \lim_{n\to+\infty} \sigma_n$$

E represents the convergence between the lower and upper integral sum. The function is therefore said to be integrable in the closed interval [a,b]. A sufficient condition for integrability is given by the continuity of the function over a closed and bounded interval: a uniformly continuous function is therefore integrable. A function is said to be absolutely integrable if its module is integrable (it goes without saying that an absolutely integrable function is integrable).

29

IV – Integral calculus

The Riemann integral enjoys the properties of linearity, additivity and monotonicity. In formulas we have:

$$\int_a^b \left[\alpha f(x) + \beta g(x)\right] dx = \alpha \int_a^b f(x)dx + \beta \int_a^b g(x)dx$$

$$\int_a^b f(x)dx = \int_a^c f(x)dx + \int_c^b f(x)dx \Leftrightarrow c \in [a,b]$$

$$\int_a^b f(x)dx \geq \int_a^b g(x)dx \Leftrightarrow f(x) \geq g(x)$$

Furthermore, two theorems concerning the absolute value and the integral mean hold:

$$\left|\int_a^b f(x)dx\right| \leq \int_a^b |f(x)|dx$$

$$\exists c \in [a,b]: \frac{1}{b-a}\int_a^b f(x)dx = f(c)$$

The Riemann integral proposed up to now is called a definite integral and it is a functional, ie it returns a numerical value following an operation on a function of a real variable.

The geometric meaning of the integral defined according to Riemann is easy to explain. Recalling that the upper integral sum is the area of the rectangles circumscribed to the region of the plane delimited by the graph of the function and the abscissa axis and that the lower integral sum is instead the area of the rectangles inscribed in this region, the definite integral computes exactly the area subtended between the graph of the function and the abscissa axis in the closed and bounded interval [a,b].

IV – Integral calculus

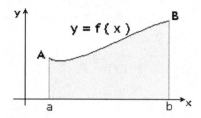

This result is also valid for the plane regions included between two curves, where the definite integral of the difference of the functions represents the measure of the area of that plane region (always keeping in mind that the geometric areas are positive and therefore we consider always the absolute values of the differences).

A further geometric application of the definite integral is given by the calculation of the volume and surface area of a solid of rotation. In fact, in the closed and bounded interval [a,b] the following holds:

$$V = \int_a^b \pi f(x)^2 \, dx$$

$$S = \int_a^b 2\pi f(x)\sqrt{1 + f'(x)^2} \, dx$$

Instead, we call integral function (or Torricelli integral) a function given by a definite integral in which one extremum of integration is fixed while the other is variable.

$$F(x) = \int_{x_0}^x f(t) \, dt$$

The fundamental theorem of integral calculus states that given an integrable function f(x) and an integral function built on it:

$$F(x) = \int_a^b f(x) \, dx$$

31

IV – Integral calculus

Then the integral function is continuous in [a,b]. Furthermore, if f(x) is continuous, the integral function is differentiable in the open range (a,b) and holds:

$$F'(x) = f(x)$$

The integral function is said to be primitive with respect to the integrand function. In this way it is seen that the integral calculus represents the inverse of the differential one. The theorem of integral calculus applied to a definite integral leads to the fundamental formula of integral calculus.

$$\int_a^b f(x)dx = F(b) - F(a)$$

By applying the fundamental theorem of integral calculus, the so-called indefinite integrals can be defined, i.e. operators that return functions whose derivatives coincide with the original integrand function. Since the derivative of a constant function is null, it means that the primitive given by an indefinite integral is calculated up to an arbitrary constant, i.e. there are infinite primitives that can be grouped into families. A sufficient condition for the existence of a primitive (and therefore of infinite primitives) is continuity in a closed and bounded interval [a,b]. From this it follows that the derivative of an integral of a function is the function itself, while the integral of the derivative is defined up to the arbitrary constant.
The following notable indefinite integrals can be defined:

$$\int [f(x)]^n f'(x)dx = \frac{[f(x)]^{n+1}}{n+1}$$

$$\int n dx = nx$$

$$\int \cos f(x) f'(x)dx = \operatorname{sen} f(x)$$

$$\int \operatorname{senf}(x) f'(x)dx = -\cos f(x)$$

$$\int \frac{f'(x)}{f(x)}dx = \ln|f(x)|$$

$$\int a^{f(x)} f'(x)dx = \frac{a^{f(x)}}{\ln a}$$

$$\int \frac{f'(x)}{\cos^2 f(x)}dx = \tan(f(x))$$

$$\int \frac{f'(x)}{\sin^2 f(x)}dx = -\cot(f(x))$$

$$\int \cosh f(x) f'(x)dx = \sinh f(x)$$

$$\int \sinh f(x) f'(x)dx = \cosh f(x)$$

$$\int \frac{f'(x)}{\cosh^2 f(x)}dx = \tanh(f(x))$$

$$\int \frac{f'(x)}{\sinh^2 f(x)}dx = -\coth(f(x))$$

$$\int \frac{f'(x)}{\sqrt{1-[f(x)]^2}}dx = \arcsin f(x) = -\arccos f(x)$$

$$\int \frac{dx}{\sin x} = \ln \left| \tan\left(\frac{x}{2}\right) \right|$$

$$\int \frac{f'(x)}{1+[f(x)]^2}dx = \arctan(x)$$

$$\int \frac{dx}{x^2+m^2} = \frac{1}{m}\arctan\left(\frac{x}{m}\right)$$

The properties ofadditivity, monotonicity, and linearity of definite integrals also apply to definite ones. For the search of the primitives, and therefore for the resolution of the integral calculus, one can go back to the notable formulas above, but also use two different methods given by integration by parts and by integration by substitution.
The integration by parts takes its cue from the derivation rule of Leibnitz and from the theorem of integral calculus, in particular we have:

$$\int f(x)g'(x)dx = f(x)g(x) - \int f'(x)g(x)dx$$

33

IV – Integral calculus

Integration by substitution is achieved by changing the integration variable by substituting a function more suitable to be integrated easily. In the case of integrals of rational functions, if the numerator has greater degree than the denominator, a polynomial division is carried out in order to isolate the quotient and the remainder (of lower degree than the denominator) in this way:

$$\int \frac{f(x)}{g(x)} dx = \int Q(x)dx + \int \frac{R(x)}{g(x)} dx$$

At this point we return to the calculation of the integral of a rational function having degree of the numerator lower than that of the denominator. If the numerator is exactly the derivative of the denominator, the integral is simply given by the natural logarithm of the function placed in the denominator.

Otherwise, if the roots of the denominator are real and distinct, a polynomial decomposition is carried out in order to apply the additivity of the integral and separate the individual rational contributions of unitary degree. If instead the roots are real and coincident, the decomposition must take into account the multiplicity of solutions, each taken with its own degree.

If, on the other hand, the roots are complex conjugates, we go back to the last notable integral presented. More generally, the Hermite decomposition can be used:

$$\int \frac{f(x)}{g(x)} dx = \frac{A}{(x-\alpha)} + \frac{(Bx+C)}{(x^2 + px + q)} + \frac{d}{dx} \frac{S(x)}{T(x)}$$

Where the first term is for real roots, the second for complex ones, while the third term has the numerator one degree lower than the denominator, which in turn has the same roots as g(x) but with multiplicity decreased by one, while the other parameters are all to be determined from time to time.

A definite integral is defined as improper if at least one of the integration extremes tends to infinity or if, within the integration domain, the integrand function is not continuous or is not defined and, at the same time, the integral exists and is finite. If, on the other hand, in these cases, the integral is infinite, it is said to diverge.

IV – Integral calculus

In the case of extrema of integration which are discontinuous of the second kind, the following limits must exist and be finite (the first in the case of an upper extremum, the second for the lower one):

$$\lim_{k \to b^-} \int_a^k f(x)dx$$

$$\lim_{h \to a^+} \int_h^b f(x)dx$$

If a point inside the integration interval is discontinuous of the second kind, the improper integral exists if the two expressions exist independently:

$$\lim_{k \to c^-} \int_a^k f(x)dx = l_1$$

$$\lim_{h \to c^+} \int_h^b f(x)dx = l_2$$

The value of the improperly defined integral is given by the sum of these limits.

In the case of improper integrals with extremes of integration at infinity, different criteria of integrability at infinity hold.

If the limit of f(x) exists as x tends to infinity, a necessary condition for the improper integral to be convergent is the vanishing of the function when x diverges.

A necessary and sufficient condition is the Cauchy criterion:

$$\forall \varepsilon > 0, \exists \gamma > 0 : \forall |x_1 - x_2| < \gamma \Rightarrow \left| \int_{x_1}^{x_2} f(x)dx \right| < \varepsilon \Leftrightarrow \exists \int_a^{+\infty} f(x)dx$$

Define instead two functions f(x) and g(x) in the open interval between a and infinity, if g(x) is greater than f(x) and is integrable, then f(x) is also integrable and if f(x) is divergent, then so is g(x). This criterion goes under the name of comparison criterion.

A different version is given by the asymptotic comparison which states that if f(x) and g(x) have infinities of the same order, then f(x) is integrable if and only if g(x) is integrable.

Finally, an improper integral converges absolutely if the improper integral of the absolute value of the integrand converges; if an improper integral is absolutely convergent then it is convergent. Some notable improper integrals are given by (the first is the Gauss integral, the second the Fresnel integral):

$$\int_0^{+\infty} e^{-\frac{x^2}{2}}\,dx = \frac{1}{2}\sqrt{\frac{\pi}{2}}$$

$$\int_{-\infty}^{+\infty} \cos(x^2)\,dx = \int_{-\infty}^{+\infty} \sin(x^2)\,dx = \sqrt{\frac{\pi}{2}}$$

$$\int_0^{+\infty} \sqrt{x}\,e^{-x}\,dx = \int_0^{+\infty} e^{-x^2}\,dx = \frac{\sqrt{\pi}}{2}$$

$$\int_{-\infty}^{+\infty} \frac{\sin x}{x}\,dx = \pi$$

Many of these improper integrals have remarkable properties which we will explain later in the manual.

The integral defined according to Riemann implies that if f(x) is continuous and integrable, both its square and its modulus are; this property does not hold for the improper definite integral.

The improper integral always represents the area of the plane region between the graph of the integrand function and the abscissa axis. If it exists and is finite it means that the area, although unlimited, has a finite value.

The Riemann integral introduced in this chapter strongly depends on the concept of measure (which is called Cauchy-Riemann) in particular on what has been said on the geometric interpretation of the measure of areas, we will see later how this concept can be extended just changing the definition of measure.

V – STUDY OF FUNCTIONS WITH REAL VARIABLES

With the notions of mathematical analysis exposed up to here, it is easy to express an algorithm for the study of functions with real variables and for tracing the graph of these functions. The algorithm consists of three successive phases: extraction of information from the function, from its first derivative and from its second derivative.

Phase 1: Information from the starting function
a) Definition set: the domain of the function is calculated by remembering that the denominators must be different from zero, the radicals of roots with even index must be greater than or equal to zero, the argument of the logarithms must be positive, the argument of tangents must be different from multiples of 90°, the arcsine and arccosine functions are between -1 and +1.
b) Determination of symmetries: a function is symmetrical with respect to the ordinate axis if it does not change its value by replacing the variable with its opposite. If, on the other hand, it assumes the opposite value, it is symmetrical with respect to the origin. A function can be symmetrical with respect to any point of the Cartesian plane or to any axis parallel to the ordinate axis. In this case, a coordinate change is applied by translating the Cartesian axes.
c) Determination of periodicity: a function is periodic if it repeats itself identically after a certain period. Typical periodic functions are the trigonometric functions.
d) Intersections with the coordinate axes: the intersection with the ordinate axis is obtained by canceling the independent variable. The intersection with the abscissa axis is obtained by solving the equation f(x)=0.
e) Sign of the function: within the definition set, the positivity set of the function is obtained by solving the inequality f(x)>0.
f) Calculation of the limits on the boundary: the limits at the boundary of the definition set are calculated. If the domain is unbounded above or below this translates into calculating limits at infinity. If it happens that these limits are finite, it means that the function has horizontal asymptotes at infinity given by horizontal lines with ordinate equal to the value of the limit. In the case in which these limits are infinite, if the function divided by x has a limit at infinity which is finite, there are oblique asymptotes whose angular coefficient is given by the value of

37

V – Study of functions with real variables

this limit. The horizontal or oblique asymptotes can be present in a maximum number of two or not be present. In the figure there are two examples:

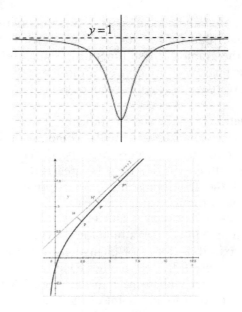

g) Determination of the points of discontinuity: the points of discontinuity of the function are identified. In case of discontinuity points of the second kind there are vertical asymptotes with abscissa equal to the value of the discontinuity point. By calculating the limit at that point and on the basis of the sign of the function, it is possible to understand whether there are infinities that agree or disagree between right and left neighbourhoods.

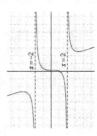

V – Study of functions with real variables

Phase 2: Information from the first derivative
a) Calculus: the first derivative of the function is calculated.
b) Definition set: the domain of the first derivative is calculated by remembering that it is contained in that of the starting function.
c) Sign of the derivative: where the first derivative is positive, the function is increasing; where it is negative, it is decreasing, where it is zero we have a stationary point.
d) Classification of stationary points: in the neighborhood of a stationary point, if the first derivative is negative in the left neighborhood and positive in the right neighborhood, there is a local minimum point. If the first derivative is positive in the left neighborhood and negative in the right one, we have a local maximum point. If the first derivative is always positive in the two neighbourhoods, there is a horizontal ascending inflection, if it is always negative in the two neighbourhoods, there is a horizontal descending inflection.

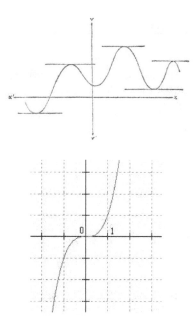

e) Classification of the discontinuity points of the first derivative: where the first derivative is not defined, but the starting function is,

39

V – Study of functions with real variables

there may be several cases. If the left and right derivatives exist and are finite but different from each other, we speak of an angular point.

If the left and right derivatives are infinite with opposite signs, we have a cusp (pointing upwards if the left derivative is positive infinity, pointing downwards if vice versa).

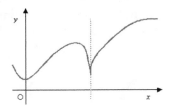

If, on the other hand, the left and right derivatives are infinite with the same sign, there is a vertical inflection (ascending if the infinities are positive, descending if vice versa).

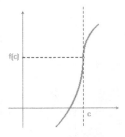

Phase 3: Information from the second derivative
a) Calculus: the second derivative of the function is calculated.
b) Definition set: the domain of the second derivative is calculated by remembering that it is contained in that of the first derivative (and therefore in that of the starting function).

c) Sign of the derivative: where the second derivative is positive the concavity is directed upwards, where it is negative it is directed downwards, while where the second derivative is zero there is an inflection point.

d) Classification of the stationary points of the second derivative: where the second derivative and the first derivative cancel each other, we have horizontal tangent inflections already found in the second phase of study of the function. Identically for vertical tangent inflections, where the second derivative is zero and the first derivative is infinite. The points where the second derivative is zero and the first derivative is finite and different from zero are inflection points with oblique tangent (ascending if the left-hand second derivative is negative, descending if vice versa). The angular coefficient of this tangent is given by the value of the first derivative at that point.

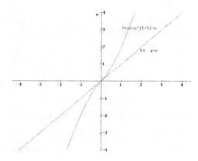

Having extracted all this information, it is possible to draw the graph of any function of a real variable.

To complete the study of functions of real variable, let us also consider integral functions:

$$F(x) := \int_{x_0}^{x} f(t)\,dt$$

Where f is a continuous function on a closed interval. From the fundamental theorem of integral calculus, the integral function is continuous and derivable and has the integrand function as its derivative.

41

V – Study of functions with real variables

In case the integration extrema coincide, the integral function is identically zero just as the second derivative of the integral function is equal to the first derivative of the integrand function. The extrema of the integral can be given by functions and in this case the rule of derivation for composite functions also applies. The study of an integral function is divided into two phases: the study of the integrand function and the study of the integral function. The study of the integrand function falls within what has already been said. The integral function is studied as follows:

a) Sign of the integral function: the value of the definite integral is calculated.
b) Calculation of the limits on the frontier: the limits at infinity of the integral function are calculated using the convergence criteria of improper integrals. If the integral diverges also the integral function diverges, if instead it converges then the integral function has a horizontal asymptote with ordinate equal to the value of this limit. If the integral diverges but the limit of the integral function divided by t converges, then the integral function has an oblique asymptote.
c) Determination of the points of discontinuity: the integral function is continuous in the points of discontinuity of the first kind of the integrand function. In the case of discontinuity points of the second kind, if the integral diverges the integral function has a vertical asymptote and is not defined for values greater than this asymptote.

By deriving and recalling the fundamental theorem of integral calculus, we go back to phases 2 and 3 for the already mentioned case of functions with real variables.

VI – ADVANCED ANALYTICAL GEOMETRY

In this chapter we will generalize what has been said about the elementary analytic geometry of the plane, going so far as to make explicit some equations and relations that expand the previous ones. At the same time, we will introduce the analytic geometry of space and projective geometry.

We define versor as a vector of unit modulus, used to indicate a particular direction and verse. Unit vectors are associated to the Cartesian axes (two in the case of the plane and three in the case of space, in this case we speak of an intrinsic triad). In Cartesian coordinates, i.e. considering the normal Cartesian axes orthogonal to each other, the three unit vectors have the subscripts x,y,z or are called i,j,k. Furthermore, each of them can be associated with a column vector of three components formed by 1 in the direction of the unit vector and by two 0 in the other directions.

We define direct cosines of a straight line as the cosines of the convex angles that the straight line forms with the Cartesian axes, both in the plane and in space. If the line is oriented, the directing cosines are uniquely identified, otherwise they change sign if the orientation of the line changes.

The general equation of a straight line in the plane considering the direction cosines is given by:

$$x \cos \alpha + y \cos \beta = p$$

In the plane, polar coordinates can be defined, in addition to the Cartesian ones, as done for the geometric interpretation of complex numbers, given by the radius and the angle subtended with the abscissa axis. The relations linking the Cartesian formulas with the polar ones are as follows:

$$x = r \cos \vartheta$$
$$y = r \sin \vartheta$$
$$r = \sqrt{x^2 + y^2}$$

VI – Advanced analytical geometry

$$\vartheta = \arctan\frac{y}{x}$$

We can therefore rewrite, in polar coordinates, the equations of analytical geometry which will be called, in this case, polar. Logically also the associated unit vectors will be those related to the new polar coordinates and not those related to the Cartesian axes. The origin of the axes is called the pole.
A radial line (that is, through the pole) is defined by this simple equation:

$$\vartheta = \varphi = \arctan m$$

A non-radial line that is perpendicular to the radial line at a point is represented by:

$$r(\vartheta) = r_0 \sec(\vartheta - \varphi)$$

The advantage of the polar coordinates in the plane is in the transition to the study of conics. A conic having one focus on the pole and the other coincident with another point on the abscissa axis, has the major axis lying on the polar axis and its equation is given by:

$$r(\theta) = \frac{l}{1 + e\cos\vartheta}$$

Where l is the perpendicular to the semimajor axis of the curve and e is the eccentricity of the curve. If the eccentricity is greater than 1 we have a hyperbola, if it is equal to 1 a parabola, if it is less than 1 an ellipse. If the eccentricity is zero the conic is reduced to a circumference of radius equal to l.
A general circle with center in a point other than the pole and radius equal to a is given by:

$$r^2 - 2rr_0\cos(\theta - \varphi) + r_0^2 = a^2$$

A hyperbola has different equations for the two branches and according to the signs of the quadrants:

$$r^2 = \pm a \sec 2\vartheta$$
$$r^2 = \pm a \csc 2\vartheta$$

In polar coordinates, the equations of other curves other than conic curves can be defined. In particular, an equation of this type defines a rodonea:

$$r = R\sin(a\vartheta)$$

Where R is a positive real number and is the maximum distance of the curve from the center of the windings, a is a positive real number which determines the shape of the curve. If a is even the figure will have a number of windings equal to twice a, if it is odd the windings will be equal to a, if a is 1 a circumference is obtained. If instead a is a rational number, the rodonea has a finite number of overlapping windings, if it is irrational the number of windings is infinite and each winding is not closed on itself. If instead of the sine function we have the cosine function we obtain an analogous but rotated figure.

Another curve is the Archimedean spiral, defined as follows:

$$r = a + b\vartheta$$

With a and b real numbers. The distance between the arms of the spiral is equal to $2\pi b$, so b must be positive.

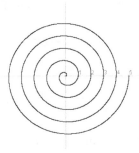

A hyperbolic spiral has a horizontal asymptote at infinity given by y=a and has this equation:

VI – Advanced analytical geometry

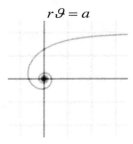

$$r\vartheta = a$$

A logarithmic spiral is given by:

$$r = ab^{\vartheta}$$

With a non-zero real number and b positive real number greater than one. The distances between the arms of the logarithmic spiral increase with geometric progression.

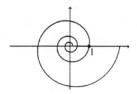

In addition to polar coordinates, parametric coordinates can be used in which the variables are expressed as a function of one or more parameters. This math application comes in very handy in physics.
A line in general form can be parametrized as follows:

$$x = x_0 + \alpha t$$
$$y = y_0 + \beta t$$
$$t = \frac{x - x_0}{\alpha}$$

A parabola whose vertex is at the origin can be parameterized as follows:

$$x = t$$
$$y = t^2$$

46

VI – Advanced analytical geometry

A circle having its center at the origin is parameterized as follows :

$$x = r\cos t$$
$$y = r\sin t$$

An ellipse with center at the origin:

$$x = a\cos t$$
$$y = b\sin t$$

A hyperbola, based on the quadrants, is given by:

$$x = a\cosh t$$
$$y = b\sinh t$$
$$x = a\sec t$$
$$y = b\tan t$$

The Archimedean spiral, the hyperbolic one and the logarithmic one are expressed as follows:

$$x = (a + bt)\cos t$$
$$y = (a + bt)\sin t$$
$$x = a\frac{\cos t}{t}$$
$$y = a\frac{\sin t}{t}$$
$$x = ae^{bt}\cos t$$
$$y = ae^{bt}\sin t$$

We call tractrix a curve whose tangent segments between the curve and a given straight line are of equal measure. The tractor can be expressed according to two types of parameterization, trigonometrically or hyperbolically. Except that the abscissa is expressed in this way:

$$x = a\left(\ln \frac{a + \sqrt{a^2 - y^2}}{y} \right) - \sqrt{a^2 - y^2}$$

The ordinate is expressed in trigonometric or hyperbolic form as follows:

$$y = a\cos t$$

$$y = \frac{a}{\cosh t}$$

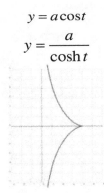

The use of polar and parametric coordinates allows not only an easy extension to curves of different nature, as seen above, but provides the elements for generalizing the elementary analytic geometry of conics having axes not parallel to the Cartesian axes, as done in Cartesian coordinates by introducing mixed terms which, however, greatly complicate the equations.

Through the use of these coordinates it is possible to study both algebraic, transcendental and diagram curves, going well beyond the concept of function of elementary analytic geometry. A plane curve is said to be algebraic if its equation in Cartesian coordinates is a polynomial equal to zero; a non-algebraic curve is transcendental. The degree of the polynomial of an algebraic curve represents its order.

In space, the three coordinates are given by abscissa, ordinate and elevation and are represented, in Cartesian coordinates, by the three coordinate axes and by the intrinsic triad. The plane identified by the origin and the unit vectors i,j is called the xy plane, the one identified by the unit vectors i,k the xz plane, the one denoted by j,k the yz plane. The general equation of a plane in Cartesian coordinates is as follows:

VI – Advanced analytical geometry

$$ax + by + cz + d = 0$$

Where a, b and c cannot all be equal to zero. The xy plane has equation z=0, the xz plane has equation y=0, the yz plane x=0. Each plane parallel to these planes has an analogous equation with a non-zero number on the second side. A plane parallel to the z axis has equation ax+by+d=0, a plane parallel to the x axis by+cz+d=0, one parallel to the y axis ax+cz+d=0. If d=0 the plane passes through the origin of the axes.

A star of plans having its center in a point has this equation:

$$a(x - x_0) + b(y - y_0) + c(z - z_0) = 0$$

A sheaf of floors is instead a linear combination of the general equation of two floors.

A plane is uniquely defined if it passes through three points and its equation is given by the determinant of the 4x4 matrix obtained from the 9 coordinates of the 3 points, the three coordinate axes and a column of 1s. If the three points lie on the coordinate axes we have the segmental equation of the plane:

$$\frac{x}{p} + \frac{y}{q} + \frac{z}{r} = 1$$

Two planes are parallel if their coefficients are in the same proportion:

$$\frac{a}{a'} = \frac{b}{b'} = \frac{c}{c'}$$

Two planes are orthogonal if it happens that:

$$aa' + bb' + cc' = 0$$

The distance of a point from a plane is as follows:

$$d = \frac{|ax_0 + by_0 + cy_0 - d|}{\sqrt{a^2 + b^2 + c^2}}$$

VI – Advanced analytical geometry

A line is the intersection of two non-parallel planes. The equation of a straight line in Cartesian coordinates is given by:

$$\frac{x - x_0}{l} = \frac{y - y_0}{m} = \frac{z - z_0}{n}$$

This straight line passes through the point P and is parallel to a vector having l,m,n as components which are called directing parameters of the straight line. This equation also represents the star of lines passing through P. The line can be expressed in parametric coordinates:

$$x = x_0 + \lambda l$$
$$y = y_0 + \lambda m$$
$$z = z_0 + \lambda n$$

The reduced equations of a straight line are as follows:

$$x = lz + p$$
$$y = mz + q$$
$$p = x_0 - lz_0$$
$$q = y_0 - mz_0$$

A line is parallel to a plane if:

$$al + bm + cn = 0$$

Two lines are coplanar if the determinant of the 4x4 matrix of the coefficients of the lines is zero. Two lines are parallel if they have the same directing parameters, they are orthogonal if:

$$l_1 l_2 + m_1 m_2 + n_1 n_2 = 0$$

For the reciprocal positions of straight lines and planes in space concepts of elementary matrix mathematics are useful, in particular all that has been said for linear systems in relation to the Rouché-Capelli theorem.

VI – Advanced analytical geometry

As far as surfaces in space are concerned, a Cartesian notation of the type can be used:

$$\varphi(x, y, z) = 0$$

Or a parametric notation:

$$x = x(u, v)$$
$$y = y(u, v)$$
$$z = z(u, v)$$

A surface is said to be ruled if it consists of a family of straight lines depending on a parameter. These lines are called generatrices. Among the ruled surfaces there are cones and cylinders: the former have generatrixes which all pass through a point, called the vertex of the cone, the latter have generatrixes which are all parallel to each other (the vertex is a point projective to infinity, as will be said soon). A curve drawn on the ruled surface that meets all the generatrixes in a single point is called a directrix.

Rotating a line around a straight line generates a surface of rotation; this straight line is called the axis of rotation. Each point on the line describes a circle, called a parallel, which lies in a plane perpendicular to the axis of rotation. The planes that pass through the axis of rotation intersect the surface according to curves symmetrical to the axis, called meridians.

A surface is said to be algebraic if its Cartesian equation is a polynomial equal to zero. the order of the surface is the degree of the polynomial, so the planes are algebraic surfaces of order 1, the quadrics of order 2.

A curve is a locus of points dependent on a parameter and can be represented as the intersection of two surfaces. A curve is said to be plane if all its points belong to a plane, vice versa it is said to be oblique. To describe surfaces and curves in space it is necessary to introduce spherical and cylindrical coordinates.

In spherical coordinates, the three parameters are given by the distance from the point to the origin, the angle between the segment connecting the point at the origin with the z axis, the angle between the x axis and the projection of the segment on the xy plane which connects the point to the origin. The links with Cartesian coordinates are given by the following relations:

$$x = r \sin \vartheta \cos \varphi$$
$$y = r \sin \vartheta \sin \varphi$$
$$z = r \cos \vartheta$$
$$r = \sqrt{x^2 + y^2 + z^2}$$
$$\varphi = \arctan \frac{y}{x}$$
$$\vartheta = \arccos \frac{z}{\sqrt{x^2 + y^2 + z^2}}$$

In cylindrical coordinates, the three parameters are given by the length of the projection on the xy plane of the segment connecting the point to the origin, by the angle between the x axis and the projection on the xy plane of the segment connecting the point to the origin and by the point height. The links with Cartesian coordinates are given by the following relations:

$$x = r \cos \varphi$$
$$y = r \sin \varphi$$
$$z = z$$
$$r = \sqrt{x^2 + y^2}$$
$$\varphi = \arctan \frac{y}{x}$$
$$z = z$$

VI – Advanced analytical geometry

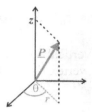

Let us consider quadrics, i.e. algebraic surfaces of order 2. Any point of a quadric can be defined as hyperbolic, parabolic or elliptic on the basis of how the tangent plane cuts the quadric itself: if in two real and distinct lines, two real and coinciding lines or two conjugate imaginary lines. All points of the same quadric are of the same type, therefore the same quadric assumes hyperbolic or parabolic or elliptical characteristics, as this is established only by the sign of the determinant of the quadric. All quadrics can be normalized, through appropriate rotations and translations, to elementary equations that we are now going to make explicit.

The non-degenerate quadrics are the ellipsoid, the spheroid, the sphere, the elliptical paraboloid, the circular one, the hyperbolic one, the hyperbolic hyperboloid and the elliptical hyperboloid.

A standard ellipsoid in Cartesian coordinates is given by:

$$\frac{x^2}{a^2} + \frac{y^2}{b^2} + \frac{z^2}{c^2} = 1$$

If at least two of the parameters are equal to each other, the ellipsoid is called a spheroid. If all the parameters are equal to each other, we have a sphere with center at the origin and radius equal to the value of the parameter.

The equation of a sphere in Cartesian coordinates having a center different from the origin is given by:

$$(x - x_0)^2 + (y - y_0)^2 + (z - z_0)^2 = R^2$$

In spherical coordinates instead it is:

$$x = x_0 + R \sin \vartheta \cos \varphi$$
$$y = y_0 + R \sin \vartheta \sin \varphi$$

53

VI – Advanced analytical geometry

$$z = z_0 + R\cos\vartheta$$

An elliptical paraboloid has vertical sections given by parabolas and its Cartesian equation, if the vertex is at the origin, is (if a=b the paraboloid is circular):

$$\frac{x^2}{a^2} + \frac{y^2}{b^2} - z = 0$$

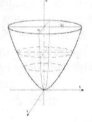

A hyperbolic paraboloid has horizontal sections given by hyperbolas and its Cartesian equation is (if the vertex is at the origin):

$$\frac{x^2}{a^2} - \frac{y^2}{b^2} - z = 0$$

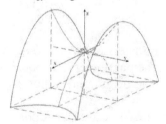

The hyperbolic hyperboloid has this Cartesian equation:

$$\frac{x^2}{a^2} + \frac{y^2}{b^2} - \frac{z^2}{c^2} = 1$$

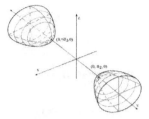

The elliptical one is the following:

$$\frac{x^2}{a^2} + \frac{y^2}{b^2} - \frac{z^2}{c^2} = -1$$

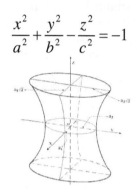

The degenerate quadrics are the cone and the four types of cylinder (elliptical, circular, hyperbolic and parabolic). The equations of the cone are:

$$\frac{x^2}{a^2} + \frac{y^2}{b^2} - \frac{z^2}{c^2} = 0$$

The elliptical cylinder is represented as follows:

$$\frac{x^2}{a^2} + \frac{y^2}{b^2} = 1$$

If a=b the cylinder is circular. The hyperbolic cylinder has the following equation:

VI – Advanced analytical geometry

$$\frac{x^2}{a^2} - \frac{y^2}{b^2} = 1$$

Finally, the parabolic one is expressed as follows:

$$x^2 + 2ay = 0$$

A final surface worthy of study is the pseudo-sphere which is a surface of rotation of a tractor around its asymptote. The pseudo-sphere has constant curvature at every point, opposite to that of the sphere of radius R. There are two possible parameterizations that reflect the different natures of the tractor, in trigonometric or hyperbolic form:

$$x = \sin t \sin a$$
$$y = \sin t \cos a$$
$$z = \cos t + \ln \tan \frac{t}{2}$$
$$x = \sec hv \sin u$$
$$y = \sec hv \cos u$$
$$z = v - \tanh v$$

We can also parametrize the two surfaces already presented in general topology. The Mobius strip of width one, centered at the origin of the axes and with the central circle lying on the xy plane, is given in Cartesian coordinates as follows:

$$x(u.v) = (1 + \frac{v}{2}\cos\frac{u}{2})\cos u$$

$$y(u.v) = (1 + \frac{v}{2}\cos\frac{u}{2})\sin u$$

$$z(u.v) = \frac{v}{2}\sin\frac{u}{2}$$

With the following limitations:

$$0 \le u < 2\pi$$
$$-1 \le v \le 1$$

Changing the u parameter moves along the tape, changing v moves from edge to edge. In cylindrical coordinates it is possible to define an infinite version of the tape, given by:

$$\log(r)\sin(\frac{\vartheta}{2}) = z\cos(\frac{\vartheta}{2})$$

A possible parametrization of the Klein bottle is the following:

$$x = \left(r + \cos\frac{u}{2}\sin v - \sin\frac{u}{2}\sin 2v\right)\cos u$$

$$y = \left(r + \cos\frac{u}{2}\sin v - \sin\frac{u}{2}\sin 2v\right)\sin u$$

$$z = \sin\frac{u}{2}\sin v + \cos\frac{u}{2}\sin 2v$$

With this parameterization, the circle of self-intersection lies on the xy plane and is a geometric circle; furthermore r is the radius of this circle, while u expresses the angle in the xy plane and v specifies the position on the section.

Advanced analytic geometry also contemplates projective geometry, i.e. the incorporation of the infinite into the geometric description.
The projective plane is the normal Euclidean plane to which is added an improper straight line positioned at infinity such that the Euclidean plane is circumscribed by it. The way to define a projective plane is essentially irrelevant since the generated structures are all isomorphic to

each other. A model is given by the sphere immersed in three-dimensional Euclidean space: the projective points of the projective plane are the pairs of antipodal points on the sphere, the projective lines are the great circles of the sphere. A pair of antipodal points on the sphere identifies a straight line in three-dimensional space passing through the origin; this straight line has parametric equations given by:

$$x = x_1 t$$
$$y = x_2 t$$
$$z = x_3 t$$

The projective plane has a system of homogeneous coordinates given by the parameters mentioned before which are in an equivalence relation with the quotient set of the Euclidean space. The projective plane is compact and connected.

A straight line in homogeneous coordinates has equation given by:

$$ax_1 + bx_2 + cx_3 = 0$$

And it has only one improper point which is as follows:

$$x_1 = b$$
$$x_2 = -a$$
$$x_3 = 0$$

All straight lines passing through the same improper point are parallel.

For the projective space similar considerations apply, in particular the cone, the cylinder and the other degenerate quadrics are equivalent to each other; the two hyperbolic paraboloids and the ruled surfaces are equivalent to each other, finally the ellipsoid, the elliptic paraboloid, the elliptic hyperboloid and the other quadrics are equivalent to each other. Instead, we refer to the study of vector spaces for further insights into n-dimensional projective spaces.

VII – NON-EUCLIDEAN GEOMETRIES

Until now, the geometry presented has always been the Euclidean one, i.e. the one that accepts Euclid's five postulates, while a geometry that does not accept one or more of Euclid's postulates is called non-Euclidean geometry. For historical reasons, non-Euclidean geometries have developed starting from the non-acceptance of Euclid's fifth postulate (also known as the parallel postulate) as its demonstration was in vain starting from the first four postulates.

Let us briefly recall that Euclid's fifth postulate in its best-known form states that, given a straight line and a point outside it, there is only one parallel to the given straight line passing through that point.

We define absolute or neutral geometry as geometry which does not assume Euclid's fifth postulate in any of its equivalent forms. In an absolute geometry, Hilbert's axioms hold, whose primitive concepts are the point, the straight line and the plane and the primitive binary relations are membership (a point may or may not be contained in a straight line or in a plane, a straight line can be contained or not in a plane), adjacency and congruence.

Hilbert's axioms can be linking:

1) Two distinct points in space identify a straight line.
2) Each pair of points of a straight line identifies this straight line.
3) Three non-aligned points in space identify a plane.
4) Any triad of non-aligned points of a plane identifies that plane.
5) If two points of a straight line lie on a plane all the points of the straight line lie on that plane.
6) If two planes have a common point they will have at least a second point in common.
7) Every straight line contains at least two points, every plane contains at least three non-aligned points, and there are at least four non-coplanar points.

By sort:

1) If a point A is between B and C, A is also between C and B, and the three points are aligned.

2) Given two distinct points *A* and *B* , there exist a third and fourth point *C* and *D* on the line passing through *A* and *B* such that *A* is between *C* and *B* and *B* is between *A* and *D*.
3) Given three distinct and aligned points, there is exactly one that lies between the other two.
4) Pasch's axiom: given three non-aligned points *A* , *B* and *C* , contained in a plane, and a straight line contained in the plane not containing any of the three points A, B, C: if the straight line contains a point of the segment *AB* , then it also contains a point of one of the segments *AC* and *BC* .

Of congruence:

1) If A, B are two points of a straight line and moreover A' is a point on the same straight line, one can always find a point B', from a given part of the straight line with respect to A', such that the segment AB is congruent to segment A'B'.
2) The congruence relation between segments is transitive.
3) Let *AB* and *BC* be segments on a straight line without common internal points, and let A'B' and B'C' be segments on another straight line without common internal points. If $AB \equiv A'B'$ and $BC \equiv B'C'$, then $AC \equiv A'C'$.
4) Let *ABC be* an angle and *B'C'* a half-line, there exist and are unique two half -*lines B'D* and *B'E* , such that the angle *DB'C'* is congruent to the angle ABC and the angle *EB'C* 'is congruent to the angle *ABC* .
5) The congruence relation between angles is transitive.
6) If for two triangles *ABC* and *A'B'C'* we have that $AB \equiv A'B'$, $AC \equiv A'C'$, and the angle $BAC \equiv$ to the angle $B'A'C'$, then all the triangle $ABC \equiv$ triangle $A'B'C'$.

Of continuity (called Dedekind's axiom):

1) If *AB* and *CD* are any two segments, then there exists on the straight line containing *AB* a family of points such that the single segments determined by these points are congruent to *CD* and such that *B* lies within the family of points.

Hilbert's axioms define a complete absolute geometry. If the axiom of parallels is also valid, we go back to Euclidean geometry.
Elliptical or Riemann geometry is a non-Euclidean geometry which replaces the parallel postulate with the following Riemann axiom: any

two straight lines in a plane always have at least one point in common. In elliptical geometry there are therefore no parallel lines and all lines perpendicular to a line meet at only one point. To define an elliptical geometry, the ordering axioms must be slightly modified, which become (the symbol S(AB|CD) is the quaternary relation that separates the pair of points AB from that CD):

1) If S (AB | CD), then A, B, C, D are four distinct points belonging to the same straight line.
2) If S (AB | CD), then: S (BA | CD); S (AB | DC); S (BA | DC); S (CD | AB); S (CD | BA); S (DC | AB); S (DC | BA).
3) If A, B, C are three points of a straight line, then there exists at least one point D such that S (AB | CD).
4) If A, B, C, D are four distinct points belonging to the same straight line, then there exists a pair of points which separates the pair formed by the other two; that is, at least one of the following relations holds: S (AB | CD), S (AC | BD), S (AD | BC).
5) If S (AB | CD) and S (AC | BE), then S (AB | DE).
6) A straight line which, passing through a vertex, enters a triangle, meets the opposite side.

In elliptical geometry, the circle is defined as the locus of points equidistant from the center, but also as the locus of points equidistant from a given straight line. The sum of the internal angles of a triangle is greater than 180°, this triangle is called an elliptical triangle and its area is given by:

$$A = R^2 (\alpha + \beta + \gamma - \pi)$$

where R is the radius of the sphere on which the elliptical triangle is built. Two elliptical triangles are congruent if they have congruent two sides and the included angle or two angles and the common side or the three sides or the three angles. The Pythagorean theorem is written in this way, having defined a the hypotenuse and b, you catheti us:

$$\cos a = \cos b \cdot \cos c$$

In elliptical geometry in space, a straight line and a plane always have a point in common, two planes always have a straight line in common, all lines perpendicular to a plane meet at a point.

VII – Non-Euclidean geometries

Spherical geometry is locally equivalent to elliptical geometry and always follows from the Riemann axiom and modifying the ordering axioms as done for elliptical geometry. In addition, the connection axioms must also be modified in this way:

1) The set of points of the plane is subdivided into pairs of points, such that each point of the plane belongs to one and only one pair and the points of each pair are distinct. One and only one straight line passes through two points that belong to distinct pairs, while several straight lines pass through the two points of the same pair.
2) On every straight line there are at least three points.
3) Not all points are on the same line.

Spherical geometry can be intuitively related to Euclidean geometry, since geometry can be constructed on a sphere in Euclidean space. The distance between two points on the sphere is the minimum segment that unites them, called geodesic. Even in spherical geometry, the sum of the interior angles of a triangle is greater than 180° and the properties listed above hold for elliptical geometry. The straight lines are given by the great circles, while the other geometric entities that are not great circles are the curves, therefore all the straight lines are congruent. Spherical triangles satisfy spherical trigonometry according to the laws of spherical cosines, spherical sines and spherical cotangents:

$$\cos c = \cos a \cos b + \sin a \sin b \cos C$$

$$\frac{\sin a}{\sin A} = \frac{\sin b}{\sin B} = \frac{\sin c}{\sin C}$$

$$\cot a = \frac{\cos c \cos B + \sin B \cot A}{\sin c} = \frac{\cos b \cos C + \sin C \cot A}{\sin b}$$

Hyperbolic geometry (also called saddle geometry or Lobachevskij geometry) is a non-Euclidean geometry obtained by replacing the parallel postulate with the hyperbolic postulate: given a straight line and a point disjointed from it, there exist at least two distinct straight lines passing through the point and parallel to the straight date. Hyperbolic geometry therefore goes in the opposite direction compared to what was done with elliptical and spherical geometries. There are various examples of hyperbolic spaces, including the Poincaré disk (the space is the one inside a circumference), the Poincaré half-space (given by the first and second quadrant of the Cartesian plane) and the three-dimensional hyperboloid model. In the hyperbolic plane, lines can be secants if they intersect at a point, vice versa they are parallel. However, there are two types of parallelism in hyperbolic geometry. Two lines are asymptotically parallel if one of the following conditions holds: the two lines have a point at infinity in common or there are pairs of points on the two lines that are arbitrarily close or there is no perpendicular line to both or there is a horocycle (curve of the hyperbolic plane orthogonal to all lines belonging to a beam) perpendicular to both. Two lines are ultra-parallel if one of the following conditions holds: the two lines do not have points at infinity in common or the distance between points is limited below or there is a line perpendicular to both or there is no horocycle perpendicular to both. Lines parallel to a given line and passing through a point form an angle, called parallelism. It can be seen that straight lines with an angle between the parallelism angle and its supplementary angle are ultra-parallel while those with angles equal to the parallelism angle and its supplementary angle are asymptotically parallel straight lines. It should be noted that hyperbolic parallelism is not an equivalence relation. In hyperbolic geometry, the sum of the interior angles of a triangle is always less than 180°. Hyperbolic trigonometry is derived from spherical trigonometry by considering a sphere of imaginary radius.

Another non-Euclidean geometry is projective geometry which models the concepts of perspective and horizon. In projective geometry there are no parallel lines and points at infinity or improper points are defined , as already done in advanced analytic geometry. The same happens for the straight line at infinity and the plane at infinity. Many classical theorems are simplified, for example the one concerning conic sections. Hyperbola, parabola, ellipse and circle are the same conic in the projective plane, the difference lies only in the way of intersection of the conic section with the straight line at infinity: the hyperbola has two points of intersection, the parabola only one, the ellipse and the circumference none. Similarly, the descriptive geometry that takes into consideration isometrics, perspectives and projections also falls within this description.

VIII – REAL FUNCTIONS WITH MULTIPLE VARIABLES

Functions of real variables with several variables are an extension of what has been said for real functions with one variable. Almost all the properties mentioned for one-variable functions remain valid (such as injectivity, surjectivity and bijectivity), except the ordering property which is not definable. The domain of a multivariate function is given by the Cartesian product of the domains calculated on the single variables.
A level set, or level curve, is the set of points such that:

$$f(x_1, x_2, ..., x_n) = c$$

The level set with c=0 is used to analyze the sign of the function in the domain.
The topological definition of limit is the same as that given for one-variable functions, the metric definition changes as follows:

$$\forall \varepsilon > 0, \exists \delta(\varepsilon, P_0) > 0 : d(P, P_0) < \delta \Rightarrow |f(P) - L| < \varepsilon$$

The limit exists if its value does not depend on the direction in which it is calculated. The same applies to continuity. A function is said to be continuous separately with respect to one of its variables if it is continuous as a function of the single variable, keeping the other constants. Separate continuity is a weaker condition than global continuity across all variables.
For a function of several variables, however, there are different concepts of derivative.
We call partial derivative the derivative carried out only on one of the variables, always defining the derivative as the limit of an incremental ratio. To distinguish the partial derivative from the total one, the symbol is used ∂. Partial derivatives of higher order return the order to the exponent of that symbol. A point is said to be simple if the first partial derivatives are continuous and not zero, but if one of the derivatives is zero or does not exist, the point is said to be singular. Partial differentiability implies separate continuity.
By extending the concept of partial derivative from a path along the coordinate axes to any path, we have the directional derivative.

VIII – Real functions with several variables

Once a generic unit vector is defined, the directional derivative along that vector is given by:

$$D_{\vec{u}} f(\vec{x}) = \lim_{h \to 0} \frac{f(\vec{x} + h\vec{u}) - f(\vec{x})}{h}$$

The directional derivative indicates the rate of change of the function with respect to the given direction.

The derivative of a function with several variables which takes into account the mutual dependence of the variables themselves is defined as the total derivative. For example we have:

$$\frac{d}{dt} f(x(t), y(t)) = \left(\frac{\partial f}{\partial x} \frac{\partial x}{\partial t} + \frac{\partial f}{\partial y} \frac{\partial y}{\partial t} \right)$$

However, differentiability is not a sufficient condition for continuity. A sufficient condition is instead given by differentiability.

A function of several variables is differentiable at a point of in an open set of n-dimensional Euclidean space R if there exists a linear map L such that the following relation holds:

$$\lim_{h \to 0} \frac{f(x_0 + h) - f(x_0) - L(x_0)h}{\|h\|} = 0$$

The total prime differential is given by the following product:

$$df(x_0) = L(x_0)h$$

While the total derivative is given by $L(x_0)$. The function is differentiable if it is differentiable at every point in its domain. The total differential theorem states that a function is differentiable at a point if all partial derivatives exist in a neighborhood of the point and if these partial derivatives are continuous. If the application is also continuous, the function is said to be continuously differentiable.

The total prime differential can also be expressed as:

66

VIII – Real functions with several variables

$$df = \sum_i \frac{\partial f}{\partial x_i} dx_i$$

Higher-order total differentials can be expressed as follows, for a function of two variables:

$$d^n f = \sum_{k=0}^{n} \binom{n}{k} \frac{\partial^k f}{\partial x^k} \frac{\partial^{n-k} f}{\partial y^{n-k}} (dx)^k (dy)^{n-k}$$

We call mixed derivatives the derivatives of order higher than the first which foresee the derivation of variables different from each other. For a function of two variables defined on an open set, if it admits continuous mixed second derivatives, Schwarz's theorem holds according to which the order of the derivation can be inverted without changing the result:

$$\frac{\partial^2 f}{\partial x \partial y} = \frac{\partial^2 f}{\partial y \partial x}$$

If a function is differentiable at a point, then all partial derivatives computed at that point exist and are continuous. The linear map defined as the sum of the first partial derivatives is a matrix m rows n columns called the Jacobian matrix and is exactly the equivalent of the previously mentioned linear map L:

$$\vec{L}(x)\vec{h} = J_f \vec{h} = \begin{bmatrix} \frac{\partial f_1}{\partial x_1} & \cdots & \frac{\partial f_1}{\partial x_n} \\ \cdots & \cdots & \cdots \\ \frac{\partial f_m}{\partial x_1} & \cdots & \frac{\partial f_m}{\partial x_n} \end{bmatrix} \vec{h}$$

If m=1, the Jacobian matrix reduces to an n-dimensional vector called gradient which indicates the direction of maximum slope of the graph of the function at a point.
If n=1 the function parametrizes a curve and its differential is a function that indicates the direction of the tangent line to the curve at the point.

VIII – Real functions with several variables

If m=n=1 the condition of differentiability coincides with that of differentiability and the Jacobian matrix is reduced to a number, equal to the derivative of the function at that point.

If m=n the Jacobian matrix is square and its determinant is known as the Jacobian. The inverse function theorem states that a continuously differentiable function is invertible if and only if its Jacobian determinant is nonzero.

If a function of several variables is differentiable, then the directional derivative exists and is equal to the scalar product between the gradient with respect to the single variable and the versor itself. The directional derivative therefore takes on a maximum value when the gradient and the unit vector are parallel and in agreement, a minimum value when they are parallel and discordant, and a null value when they are perpendicular.

A differential is said to be exact if and only if it is integrable, ie if it can be expressed as a function of the second class of simply connected continuity (in other words, Schwarz's theorem must hold).

We define gradient as the quantity which, multiplied according to the scalar product with any vector, returns the directional derivative of the function with respect to the vector. The gradient is a vector field and, in the case of a Cartesian reference system, it is the sum of the products between the first partial derivatives and versors:

$$grad(f) = \nabla f = \sum_i \frac{\partial f}{\partial x_i} \vec{x}_i$$

Where in the second member there is the notation according to the nabla operator. This differential operator is defined as follows:

$$\nabla = \sum_{i=1}^{n} \frac{\partial}{\partial x_i} \vec{x}_i$$

We define the divergence of a continuous and differentiable vector field as the scalar function given by the dot product between the operator nabla and the vector field:

$$div(\vec{f}) = \nabla \cdot \vec{f} = \sum_{i=1}^{n} \frac{\partial f_i}{\partial x_i}$$

VIII – Real functions with several variables

We define curl of a continuous and differentiable vector field, a vector field given by the vector product between the operator nabla and the field itself:

$$rot(\vec{f}) = \nabla \times \vec{f}$$

We define Laplacian the square of the nabla operator equal to:

$$lapl(\vec{f}) = \nabla^2 \vec{f} = \sum_{i=1}^{n} \frac{\partial^2 f_i}{\partial x_i^2} \vec{x}_i$$

Some properties of the nabla operator are as follows:

$$rot(grad(f)) = 0$$
$$div(rot(\vec{f})) = 0$$
$$div(grad(f)) = lapl(f)$$
$$div(a\vec{f}) = a\,div(\vec{f}) + grad(a) \cdot \vec{f}$$
$$div(\vec{f} \times \vec{g}) = \vec{g} \cdot rot(\vec{f}) - \vec{f} \cdot rot(\vec{g})$$
$$rot(a\vec{f}) = a\,rot(\vec{f}) + grad(a) \times \vec{f}$$
$$rot(rot(\vec{f})) = grad(div(\vec{f})) - lapl(\vec{f})$$

If all second partial derivatives exist, we define the Jacobian matrix of the gradient as Hessian of the function:

$$H_f = \begin{bmatrix} \dfrac{\partial^2 f}{\partial x_1^2} & \dfrac{\partial^2 f}{\partial x_1 \partial x_2} & \cdots & \dfrac{\partial^2 f}{\partial x_1 \partial x_n} \\ \dfrac{\partial^2 f}{\partial x_2 \partial x_1} & \dfrac{\partial^2 f}{\partial x_2^2} & \cdots & \dfrac{\partial^2 f}{\partial x_2 \partial x_n} \\ \cdots & \cdots & \cdots & \cdots \\ \dfrac{\partial^2 f}{\partial x_n \partial x_1} & \dfrac{\partial^2 f}{\partial x_n \partial x_2} & \cdots & \dfrac{\partial^2 f}{\partial x_n^2} \end{bmatrix} = J_f \cdot \nabla f$$

VIII – Real functions with several variables

If all second derivatives are continuous, Schwarz's theorem holds and the Hessian matrix is symmetric.

If the gradient of the function is zero at a point then that point is called a critical point. If at that point also the determinant of the Hessian matrix is zero then the critical point is called degenerate.

For a non-degenerate critical point, if the Hessian matrix is positive definite then the function has a local minimum at that point, if instead it is negative definite there is a local maximum.

If the Hessian matrix has all non-zero eigenvalues, and they assume both positive and negative values, that point is called a saddle point.

In all other cases, for example for positive or negative semidefinite Hessian matrices, nothing can be said about the presence of stationary points.

A necessary condition for the search for constrained maxima and minima is the so-called Lagrange multiplier method. For a two-dimensional function, this method states that the necessary condition for having a constrained extremum is that:

$$\nabla h(x_0, y_0, \lambda) = \nabla(g(x_0, y_0) + \lambda f(x_0, y_0)) = 0$$

The values of λ are precisely the Lagrange multipliers since the function h can be defined as the Lagrangian of the system. A practical case of application of this formalism is that of Lagrangian mechanics in which the equations of motion are obtained by finding the stationary points of an integral, called action.

IX – IMPLIED FUNCTIONS

Implicit functions are functions of the type:

$$f(x_1, x_2, \ldots, x_n) = 0$$

For two-dimensional functions the following Dini theorem holds. Considering a continuously differentiable function defined on an open set and a non-empty set in which the function f(x,y) is zero, then there exists a point in this set where the following relation holds:

$$f(x_0, y_0) = 0$$

If this point is not critical, i.e. the inequality holds:

$$\nabla f(x_0, y_0) \neq 0$$

Then there exists a neighborhood of this point such that the set given by the intersection of this neighborhood and the set in which the non-critical point is located represents the graph of a differentiable function. This is equivalent to saying that there is a single explicit function of the type y=y(x) or x=x(y) which relates the two unknowns. This theorem therefore provides a sufficient condition for the explicitation of the implicit functions.

In multiple dimensions, the function variables can be divided into two blocks, one up to the nth degree and one up to the mth degree, as follows:

$$(x, y) = (x_1, x_2, \ldots, x_n, y_1, y_2, \ldots, y_m)$$

The Jacobian matrix computed in the n+m-dimensional open set can be divided into two blocks, recalling the division of variables:

$$J_f(a,b) = [X \mid Y]$$

IX – Implicit functions

Assuming that X is invertible. The implicit function theorem states that there is a unique explicitation of the function f(x,y)=0. This function g(y)=x is continuously differentiable and the relation holds:

$$J_G = -X^{-1}Y$$

X – ADVANCED VECTOR AND MATRIX MATHEMATICS

A vector field is a function that associates an open and connected set of n-dimensional R with n-dimensional R itself. Generally the requirement on the function is that it be continuous and differentiable at least for a certain number of times. This function therefore associates a point of a Euclidean space with a vector of the space and, thanks to Helmoltz's theorem, a vector field is uniquely defined once the curl and divergence operations are known. Each vector field is characterized by flux lines, i.e. by curves which follow the identified directions of the vector field at each point. If the field is differentiable then one and only one flux line passes through each point.

To define a vector space some advanced algebraic concepts are needed, which will be introduced later. For now, let's say that, given an algebraic structure called a field and 0 and 1 being the zero and unity of the field, a vector space exists if an internal binary operation is defined for which this space is a commutative group. Furthermore, there is a law of internal composition, called external product, for which the associative properties exist, of neutrality with respect to unity and distributive with respect to addition.

This algebraic structure is called vector space and its elements are called vectors, while the elements of the field are called scalars. If the field is the set of real numbers, the vector space is called real; similarly we have if the field is given by the set of complex numbers.

Polynomials, matrices, n-dimensional scalars, and functions are all examples of vector spaces.

A subset of the vector space in which the operations of addition and multiplication by a scalar are closed in it is called a vector subspace. The empty set and the vector space itself are subspaces, called improper or trivial. From what has been said before, examples of vector subspaces are the mxn matrices, a straight line or a plane passing through the origin, the solutions of a homogeneous linear system, the diagonal, symmetric, antisymmetric and square matrices, the set of continuous functions or that of differentiable functions.

The intersection of two subspaces is still a subspace, while the union between subspaces is a subspace if and only if one of the two subspaces is included in the other.

The basis of a vector space is a linear combination of vectors such that they are linearly independent and generate the vector space itself. Given

73

X – Advanced vector and matrix math

any space vector, the coefficients of the single components of the basis are the coordinates of the vector with respect to the chosen basis. The basis is therefore the minimum number of linearly independent vectors that generate the space. If the set has infinitely many elements, then the possible bases are infinite. For every vector space, there is always at least one basis. The set of vectors whose components are all zero except the i-th position equal to one is called the canonical basis.

The number of vectors that make up the basis is the cardinality, or dimension, of the vector space. The dimension theorem of vector spaces states that all bases of the same vector space have the same dimension. If the vector space is finite, the dimension of the space is finite, furthermore the dimension of an n-dimensional vector space is just n. The dimension of a vector space depends on the field on which it is defined, in fact complex numbers have dimension 2 if they are defined on the real field, while they have dimension 1 if they are defined on the complex field. The mxn matrices have a dimension given by the product of the number of rows by the number of columns. A vector subspace has dimension less than or equal to the starting vector space. Two vector spaces having the same dimension are called isomorphic.

For infinite-dimensional vector spaces there are two different basic concepts. The Hamel basis is a combination of linearly independent vectors such that each vector is a linear combination of a finite set of indices of an ordered set. The Schauder basis is a linear combination of linearly independent vectors such that the generated space is dense in the starting vector space. This basis can be expressed as a limit of infinite sums.

The different definition of these bases brings with it their different dimension. In particular the dimension of Hamel can be higher than that of Schauder.

Given a vector space V and a subspace U, we can define the quotient space as the set determined by the following equivalence relation:

$$v \approx v' \Leftrightarrow v - v' \in U$$

The dimension of the quotient space, called the codimension, is the difference in dimension between the vector space and the subspace, provided that the vector space is finite dimensional.

X – Advanced vector and matrix math

A vector space V is defined as a direct sum of two subspaces U and W if every vector belonging to V can be written as the sum of vectors belonging to the two subspaces. The direct sum is expressed as follows:

$$V = U \oplus W$$

In this case, the two sum vectors belonging to the single subspaces are called projections of the vector on the single subspace. In the presence of direct sum, the quotient space between V and U is isomorphic to W. Grassmann's formula states that the dimension of a vector space in relation to two subspaces is as follows:

$$\dim V = \dim(W + U) = \dim W + \dim U - \dim(W \cap U)$$

In the presence of direct sum, the last term vanishes and the dimension of the space coincides with the sum of the dimensions of the individual subspaces.

Given a generic linear combination between vectors, if the field on which the vector space is defined is that of real numbers, the combination is called positive if all the coefficients are positive or equal to zero. If the sum of all the coefficients equals 1, the combination is said to be affine. A positive and affine linear combination is called convex.

A linear combination of vectors that generates the subspace is called linear cover. If the number of cover vectors is equal to the dimension of the subspace, the set of generators is a basis of the subspace.

Given a linear map between vector spaces, the so-called rank theorem holds:

$$\dim \operatorname{Im}(f) + \dim Ker(f) = n$$

Where Im(f) is the image of the linear map and Ker(f) is its core, while n is the dimension of the starting vector space. This theorem has a dual in the matrix field given by the following relation:

$$rank(A) + null(A) = n$$

A linear functional is a linear map between a vector space V and a field K. The set of all linear functionals forms a vector space, called dual space. If A is a matrix associated with the linear transformation with respect to two bases of two vector spaces, then the transposed matrix of A is the one associated with the linear transformation with respect to two bases of the dual spaces. If the vector space has finite dimension, the dual space is isomorphic to it. However, the isomorphism requires a certain choice on the basis so that each isomorphism is defined by a non-degenerate bilinear form. It is called dual space, the dual space of the dual space. A topological dual space is the topological vector space which is the space of linear and continuous functionals.

If the vector space has finite dimension, then the dual space has the same dimension. It is possible to define a dual basis, i.e. a basis of the dual space defined as follows:

$$e^i(e_j) = 1 \Leftrightarrow i = j$$
$$e^i(e_j) = 0 \Leftrightarrow i \neq j$$

The elements of the dual space are called covectors. The components of a vector with respect to the canonical basis are called contravariant components while the components of a map with respect to the dual basis are called covariant components.

Given two bases of a vector space and an invertible matrix representing the change of basis, the contravariant transformation is simply one that matches a vector in one basis with the product of the inverse matrix of the change of basis and the vector expressed in the other basis, while the covariant transformation is the one that links the linear functional expressed in one basis with that expressed in another basis through the basis change matrix. Contravariant and covariant descriptions are complementary and the following equality always holds:

$$\vec{v} = \sum_{i=1}^{n} v^i \vec{e}_i = \sum_{i=1}^{n} v_i \vec{e}^i$$

Where the contravariant components are on the first side and the covariant ones on the second.

We define the covariant derivative of a vector field X with respect to another vector field Y as the operator that acts between the Cartesian product of X and Y and returns the result to X. This derivative is indicated as follows: $\nabla_X Y$. If X is a vector the covariant derivative of a vector field is computed with respect to the vector.

X – Advanced vector and matrix math

An affine space is a set of elements called affine points which is endowed with a valued function in a vector space V over a field K. This function associates a vector between two affine points which is a bijection. Furthermore, for every triad of affine points, the law of additivity holds. Every vector space is an affine space having itself as an associated vector space. In an affine space it is possible to define subspaces and bases, called affine. Two affine subspaces are said to be incident when their intersection is not empty, parallel when one of the two is contained in the other, oblique when the intersection is empty and the two subspaces intersect only at the origin. Grassmann's formula does not hold for affine subspaces.

Given a vector space V, a field K with dot product and a subset W of V, then the orthogonal subspace of W is the set of vectors orthogonal to all vectors of W. The orthogonal subspace is a vector subspace of V.

Generally we have that:

$$\dim W + \dim W^{\perp} \geq \dim V$$

Where equality holds only in the case of a non-degenerate scalar product. If the dot product is positive definite, the space W and its orthogonal are in direct sum. The following relations hold for two generic subspaces:

$$U \subset W \Rightarrow W^{\perp} \subset U^{\perp}$$
$$(U + W)^{\perp} = U^{\perp} \cap W^{\perp}$$
$$(U^{\perp})^{\perp} \supset U$$

If the dot product is non-degenerate, then the orthogonal of an orthogonal is equal to the starting subspace. We define the radical of the dot product as the subspace formed by the vectors which are orthogonal to any vector in the space. A dot product is non-degenerate if and only if the radical is the empty set.

An orthogonal basis is a basis composed of pairwise orthogonal vectors. If the scalar product is positive definite, an orthonormal basis is an orthogonal basis in which each vector has unitary norm, i.e.:

$$\langle \vec{v}_i, \vec{v}_j \rangle = \delta_{ij}$$

77

X – Advanced vector and matrix math

The canonical basis is an orthonormal basis. Given two different bases it is possible to associate a matrix for the change of base. The matrix for the change between orthonormal bases is an orthogonal matrix. The mxn matrix has in the i-th column the coordinates of the vector of the linear transformation between one space and another. The linear transformation T, the bases B and C, the transformation matrix M are related as follows:

$$[T(\vec{v})]_C = M[\vec{v}]_B$$

A composition of several linear transformations results in a multiplication of the transformation matrices. If M is a square matrix we have an endomorphism; if M is the identity matrix, T is the identity transformation; if M is invertible, T is bijective; if the determinant of M is positive, T is orientation-preserving; finally, two similar matrices represent the same endomorphism with respect to two different bases.

A block matrix is a matrix whose elements are grouped into rectangular blocks defined by sub-matrices: in block matrices it is particularly easy to carry out the multiplication operation between matrices.

A triangular block matrix is a square matrix that has square blocks on the diagonal and whose blocks above or below the main diagonal contain only zeros. A block diagonal matrix has non-zero entries on the diagonal, while all others are zero. This matrix is the result of a direct sum of submatrices each of which acts on a particular vector subspace.

Given a linear transformation T of a vector space V, if there exists a basis of V with respect to which the transformation matrix is diagonal, then T is said to be diagonalizable. The basis that diagonalizes a linear transformation is composed of its eigenvectors. If T is normal and diagonalizable then the basis of V is orthonormal.

The space generated by the eigenvectors having the eigenvalues as coefficients is called the eigenspace. The dimension of the eigenspace is called geometric multiplicity, while the algebraic multiplicity is that relating to the multiplicity of the eigenvalues calculated from the characteristic polynomial. The diagonalizability theorem states that a linear transformation is diagonalizable if and only if the sum of the algebraic multiplicities is equal to n and the algebraic and geometric multiplicities of each eigenvalue are coincident. Thus if the characteristic polynomial has n distinct roots within the field, the linear transformation is diagonalizable.

X – Advanced vector and matrix math

The Jordan canonical form of a square matrix is a triangular matrix similar to a diagonal matrix. If the matrix is diagonalizable, then the canonical Jordan form is a diagonal matrix, otherwise it is divided into blocks, called Jordan blocks. Each Jordan block is an upper triangular matrix with k rows in which each element of the diagonal is equal to a given value and which has 1 inpositions (i,i+1). The characteristic polynomial of this block has a single eigenvalue, equal to the value present on the diagonal with algebraic multiplicity equal to k. A Jordan matrix is a matrix composed of various Jordan blocks and such a matrix is diagonalizable if and only if all Jordan blocks have order equal to one.

Jordan's theorem states that every matrix has a canonical Jordan form. Furthermore, two matrices are similar if and only if they have the same canonical form. Starting from the canonical form, the minimum polynomial can be obtained:

$$m(x) = (x - \lambda_1)^{j_1} ... (x - \lambda_k)^{j_k}$$

We call orthogonal projection matrix a square matrix which is equal to its square.

We can derive a method, called Gram-Schmidt orthogonalization, to derive linearly independent vectors which are orthonormal and which generate an orthonormal basis starting from any basis. For the generic vector it is a question of subtracting the orthogonal projection of that vector onto another vector and then of normalizing everything:

$$\vec{e}_k = \frac{\vec{u}_k}{\|\vec{u}_k\|} = \frac{\vec{v}_k - \sum_{j=1}^{k-1} proj_{\vec{u}_j} \vec{v}_k}{\left\| \vec{v}_k - \sum_{j=1}^{k-1} proj_{\vec{u}_j} \vec{v}_k \right\|}$$

Two orthogonal vectors have zero scalar product. The dot product can be identified by a symmetric matrix: the properties of the dot product and of the orthogonal bases are transferred to the associated matrix. Two scalar products are isometric if they are related by isometry, i.e. by a one-to-one linear transformation in the form of an automorphism.

We define the triad of numbers given by the number of base vectors such that the scalar product is positive, negative or zero, respectively.

X – Advanced vector and matrix math

Sylvester's real theorem states that, given a dot product on a real vector space V of dimension n, there exists an orthogonal basis for V. Furthermore, two orthogonal basis have the same signature and two dot products with the same signature are isomorphic.

The complex Sylvester theorem states that, given a dot product on a complex vector space V of dimension n, there exists an orthogonal basis for V. Moreover two orthogonal basis contain the same number of isotropic vectors equal to the dimension of the radical and two dot products with the same rank are isomorphic.

Given two vectors, the tensor product is the matrix mxn defined by the Kronecker product which coincides with a tensor of rank 1. The symbol of the tensor product is as follows $\vec{v} \otimes \vec{w}$.

The Kronecker matrix product is defined as follows:

$$A \otimes B = \begin{bmatrix} a_{11}B & ... & a_{1n}B \\ ... & ... & ... \\ a_{m1}B & ... & a_{nn}B \end{bmatrix}$$

This product is bilinear and associative, while it is not commutative. There exist permutation matrices P and Q such that two matrices A and B are commutative by permutation:

$$A \otimes B = P(B \otimes A)Q$$

If A and B are square matrices, then they are similar by permutation. The Kronecker product is invertible if and only if both A and B are invertible and the inverse of the product equals the product of the inverses. Furthermore, if A and B are squares of order neq we have that:

$$tr(A \otimes B) = trA \cdot trB$$
$$\det(A \otimes B) = (\det A)^q \cdot (\det B)^n$$
$$rank(A \otimes B) = rankA \cdot rankB$$

XI – DIFFERENTIAL GEOMETRY

Differential geometry is concerned with the study of geometric objects through mathematical analysis. At the basis of differential geometry is the notion of differentiable manifold which generalizes both the concepts of curve and surface in a space of any dimension and the approach given by topological manifolds. Let's say right away that, for a complete understanding of differential geometry, it is necessary to introduce the tensor vision and this will be done in the next chapter.

The differentiable manifolds also represent the connection with the differential topology in fact they are topological spaces and, locally, Euclidean spaces which are connected to each other through differentiable functions.

Considering a topological variety, the open sets that make up its cover can be related to an open set of Euclidean space through a set of homeomorphisms to which we give the name of atlas (while the single homeomorphism is called map). The composition of functions consisting of a card and its inverse function is called a transition function. A topological manifold is differentiable if the transition function is differentiable.

A differentiable submanifold in a differentiable manifold is a subset which is described as zero of a differentiable function. In the case of submanifolds with codomain equal to the set of real numbers we speak of a hypersurface and the condition of differentiability is equivalent to requiring that the gradient of the submanifold on each map is everywhere different from zero.

We define exterior product in a vector space, a product of associative and bilinear vectors:

$$\forall v \in V \,|\, v \wedge v = 0$$
$$\forall u, v \in V \,|\, u \wedge v = -v \wedge u$$
$$\forall v_1, \ldots, v_k \in V \,|\, v_1 \wedge v_2 \wedge \ldots \wedge v_k = 0 \Leftrightarrow v_1, \ldots, v_k \text{ are linearly dependent}$$

A differential form defined on an open set is given by the following expression:

$$\omega = \sum_{1 \le i_1 < ... < i_k \le n} a_{i_1,...,i_k}(x)dx_{i_1} \wedge ... \wedge dx_{i_k}$$

With functions given by differentiable functions. The form is said to be of order k. A zero order form is a differentiable function defined on the reference set. Two forms of order k can be added or multiplied by a scalar, thus giving rise to a vector space. It is also possible to define an external product between two forms having different orders and the differential form of the product is given by a form having order equal to the sum of the previous orders.

The derivative of a form of order k is a form of order k+1. This derivative is called external. The exterior derivative of a form of zero order coincides with the differential of the function. A differential form is closed if and only if:

$$d\omega = 0$$

Every form that has constant coefficients is closed. A form of order k is said to be exact if there exists a form of order k-1 such that:

$$d\eta = \omega$$

The k-1 order form is said to be primitive of the k order form. Every exact form is a closed form. A form is linear if it can be expressed as a linear combination. A linear differential form of order 1 is closed if and only if:

$$\forall i, j \mid \frac{\partial a_j}{\partial x_i} = \frac{\partial a_i}{\partial x_j}$$

If the open set is simply connected, every order 1 linear form that is closed is also exact.

A linear form on several orders is called multilinear, in particular it is called bilinear if it is of order 2. The determinant and the trace of a matrix are examples of multilinear forms.

A form of order k can be integrated over any differentiable submanifold S of dimension k. The integral looks like this and returns a real number:

XI – Differential geometry

$$\int_S \omega$$

One can always redefine the integration domain so that the integral contains the Jacobian determinant. The integral of a differential form enjoys the properties of linearity and additivity, moreover it changes sign if the orientation of the manifold changes.

A Frenet system is a reference system of n orthonormal vectors describing a regular curve, i.e. a curve having the n-th derivatives linearly independent, and therefore forming a basis. We define generalized curvatures as the dot products of these orthonormal vectors, divided by the modulus of the first derivative of the curve:

$$\chi_i(x) = \frac{\langle \vec{e}_i'(x), \vec{e}_{i+1}'(x) \rangle}{|f'(x)|}$$

In two dimensions, the first Frenet vector is the tangent to the curve at the point, while the second vector is called the normal vector and is the vector perpendicular to the tangent vector at the point under consideration. The first curvature is the displacement of the curve from the tangent line, the reciprocal of the first curvature is the radius of curvature. A circle has constant curvature, while a straight line has zero curvature. We call the osculating circle the circle tangent to the tangent vector with radius equal to the reciprocal of the first curvature.

In three dimensions the tangent vector and the normal vector are defined as follows:

$$\vec{e}_1(x) = \frac{f'(x)}{|f'(x)|}$$

$$\vec{e}_2(x) = f''(x) - \langle f''(x), \vec{e}_1(x) \rangle \vec{e}_1(x)$$

These two vectors form a plane called the osculating plane of the curve at the point x. The binormal vector is the third Frenet vector and is orthogonal to the osculating plane, defined as follows:

$$\vec{e}_3(x) = \vec{e}_1(x) \times \vec{e}_2(x)$$

XI – Differential geometry

The first generalized curvature and the radius of curvature are defined as in the two-dimensional case. The second generalized curvature is called torsion and measures how far the curve goes out of the osculating plane. A curve has zero torsion if and only if it is a plane curve. The Frenet system is the solution of the Frenet-Serret formulas which are differential equations:

$$
\begin{bmatrix} \vec{e}_1'(x) \\ \dots \\ \dots \\ \vec{e}_n'(x) \end{bmatrix}
=
\begin{bmatrix} 0 & \chi_1(x) & \dots & & 0 \\ -\chi_1(x) & \dots & & \dots & 0 \\ \dots & \dots & & 0 & \chi_{n-1}(x) \\ 0 & \dots & & -\chi_{n-1}(x) & 0 \end{bmatrix}
\begin{bmatrix} \vec{e}_1(x) \\ \dots \\ \dots \\ \vec{e}_1(x) \end{bmatrix}
$$

Given a curve, its length in a closed interval is defined as follows:

$$
L = \int_a^b |f'(x)| dx
$$

The length does not change if the curve is parameterized in any other way.

For a plane curve, the formula in Cartesian coordinates is as follows:

$$
L = \int_a^b \sqrt{1 + (f'(x))^2}\, dx
$$

In polar coordinates the length is instead:

$$
L = \int_c^d \sqrt{r(\vartheta)^2 + (f'(x))^2}\, d\vartheta
$$

Having obviously redefined the extremes of integration. We can use a particular parametrization of the curve so that the integral has only the upper bound which depends on x. This parameterization is called the curvilinear abscissa and represents the length of the arc of the curve starting from a fixed point.

For a curve in space, the sufficient condition for local regularity is given by the non-nullity of the Jacobian determinant. A curve in space is entirely defined by the previously stated parameters of curvature and torsion.

We define geodesic the curve which locally describes the shortest path in a given space. A geodesic is complete if it can extend indefinitely in both directions: for example, in a Euclidean plane, the geodesics are straight lines. In spherical geometry there are no parallel geodesics, while in hyperbolic geometry there are infinitely many. A closed geodesic is a curve defined on the circumference.

Given a differentiable manifold contained in a Euclidean space, the tangent space to a point is the space formed by the tangent vectors to all the curves of the manifold passing through that point. It can be seen that the tangency between curves is an equivalence relation and that the equivalence classes are precisely the tangent vectors.

A differentiable map between manifolds induces a linear transformation between the corresponding tangent spaces. This map is called total or differential derivative and if a manifold coincides with R, then we have the usual definition of differential. The tangent vectors are therefore the generalizations of the directional derivatives.

We define line integral of the first kind as an integral of a scalar field along a curve defined in parametric form in an open set. The line integral of the first kind is:

$$\int_\Gamma f(x,y,z)ds = \int_a^b f(\phi(t))|\phi'(t)|dt$$

Where ds is the curvilinear abscissa, Γ it is the curve along which the integral is calculated and it $\phi(t)$ represents the parametrization of the scalar function. The line integral of the first kind enjoys the properties of linearity, additivity and monotonicity. In addition, the following surcharges apply:

$$\left|\int_\Gamma fds\right| \le \int_\Gamma |f|ds \le \max_\Gamma |f| \cdot L(\Gamma)$$

If the domain of the function is R, the curvilinear integral of the first kind is the normal Riemann integral.

The line integral of the second kind is the integral of a vector field along a curve. This integral is equal to the scalar product between the vector field and the unit vector tangent to the curve:

$$\int_\Gamma \vec{F} = \int_\Gamma \vec{F}(x, y, z) \cdot \vec{T}(x, y, z) ds$$

The integral is also called work because in physics it expresses the work of a force along a path. This integral has the same properties as that of the first kind, moreover it is independent of the parametric representation adopted, except for the direction of travel which causes the sign to change.

If the vector field can be expressed as a gradient of a scalar field, i.e. if:

$$\vec{F} = \nabla G$$

then the fundamental theorem of calculus for line integrals states that the line integral can be calculated simply by evaluating the scalar field at the extremes of the curve on which the integration took place:

$$\int_\Gamma \vec{F} = \int_\Gamma \vec{F}(x, y, z) \cdot \vec{T}(x, y, z) ds = \int_\Gamma \nabla G \cdot \vec{T}(x, y, z) ds = \int_a^b \frac{dG(r(t))}{dt} dt = G(r(b)) - G(r(a))$$

This theorem is also known as the gradient theorem.

When the curve on which it integrates is closed then the line integral of the second kind takes the name of circuitry and is indicated as follows:

$$\oint_\Gamma \vec{F}$$

More generally, the circuitry is the curvilinear integral of a differential form over a closed curve. If the differential form is exact, the circuitry is zero calculated on any curve. Furthermore, if the differential form is exact, the same result given by the gradient theorem holds.

A vector field in which the gradient theorem holds and in which the circuit is zero is called a conservative field.

A vector field in which the curl is zero is called an irrotational field. Irrotality is a necessary condition for the conservatism of a vector field. We explain the nabla algebra for three-dimensional functions. In Cartesian coordinates, the gradient, divergence, curl and Laplacian are given by:

XI – Differential geometry

$$\nabla f = \frac{\partial f}{\partial x} e_x + \frac{\partial f}{\partial y} e_y + \frac{\partial f}{\partial z} e_z$$

$$\nabla \cdot a = \frac{\partial a_x}{\partial x} + \frac{\partial a_y}{\partial y} + \frac{\partial a_z}{\partial z}$$

$$\nabla \times a = (\frac{\partial a_z}{\partial y} - \frac{\partial a_y}{\partial z})e_x + (\frac{\partial a_x}{\partial z} - \frac{\partial a_z}{\partial x})e_y + (\frac{\partial a_y}{\partial x} - \frac{\partial a_x}{\partial y})e_z$$

$$\nabla^2 f = \frac{\partial^2 f}{\partial x^2} + \frac{\partial^2 f}{\partial y^2} + \frac{\partial^2 f}{\partial z^2}$$

In cylindrical coordinates we have:

$$\nabla f = \frac{\partial f}{\partial r} e_r + \frac{1}{r}\frac{\partial f}{\partial \varphi} e_\varphi + \frac{\partial f}{\partial z} e_z$$

$$\nabla \cdot a = \frac{\partial a_r}{\partial r} + \frac{a_r}{r} + \frac{1}{r}\frac{\partial a_\varphi}{\partial \varphi} + \frac{\partial a_z}{\partial z} \text{u}$$

$$\nabla \times a = (\frac{1}{r}\frac{\partial a_z}{\partial \varphi} - \frac{\partial a_\varphi}{\partial z})e_r + (\frac{\partial a_r}{\partial z} - \frac{\partial a_z}{\partial r})e_\varphi + (\frac{\partial a_\varphi}{\partial r} + \frac{a_\varphi}{r} - \frac{1}{r}\frac{\partial a_r}{\partial \varphi})e_z$$

$$\nabla^2 f = \frac{\partial^2 f}{\partial r^2} + \frac{1}{r}\frac{\partial f}{\partial r} + \frac{1}{r^2}\frac{\partial^2 f}{\partial \varphi^2} + \frac{\partial^2 f}{\partial z^2}$$

Finally in spherical coordinates:

$$\nabla f = \frac{\partial f}{\partial r} e_r + \frac{1}{r}\frac{\partial f}{\partial \vartheta} e_\vartheta + \frac{1}{r\sin\vartheta}\frac{\partial f}{\partial \varphi} e_\varphi$$

$$\nabla \cdot a = \frac{\partial a_r}{\partial r} + \frac{2a_r}{r} + \frac{1}{r}\frac{\partial a_\theta}{\partial \vartheta} + \frac{1}{r\sin\vartheta}\frac{\partial a_\varphi}{\partial \varphi}$$

$$\nabla \times a = (\frac{1}{r}\frac{\partial a_\varphi}{\partial \vartheta} + \frac{a_\vartheta}{r\tan\vartheta} - \frac{1}{r\sin\vartheta}\frac{\partial a_\vartheta}{\partial \varphi})e_r + (\frac{1}{r\sin\vartheta}\frac{\partial a_r}{\partial \varphi} - \frac{\partial a_\varphi}{\partial r} - \frac{a_\varphi}{r})e_\vartheta + (\frac{\partial a_\vartheta}{\partial r} + \frac{a_\vartheta}{r} - \frac{1}{r}\frac{\partial a_r}{\partial \vartheta})e_\varphi$$

$$\nabla^2 f = \frac{\partial^2 f}{\partial r^2} + \frac{2}{r}\frac{\partial f}{\partial r} + \frac{1}{r^2}\frac{\partial^2 f}{\partial \vartheta^2} + \frac{1}{r^2\tan\vartheta}\frac{\partial f}{\partial \vartheta} + \frac{1}{r^2\sin^2\vartheta}\frac{\partial^2 f}{\partial \varphi^2}$$

XI – Differential geometry

XII – TENSORIAL MATHEMATICS

Given a vector space V of dimension n over a field K, the dual space of V is the vector space formed by all linear functionals mapping V to K and has dimension n. The elements of V are called vectors, those of the dual space covectors. We define a tensor as a multilinear map which associates h vectors and k covectors with a scalar over the field K. Multilinearity guarantees that the function is linear in each component. A tensor thus defined has order given by the pair (h,k). The set of all tensors of the same order gives rise to a vector space of dimension equal to n^{h+k}.

A tensor of order (h,k) is described by an associated matrix, called a grid, of dimension h+k. To describe the tensor in these coordinates it is necessary to fix a basis, since different bases form different grids, therefore different components of the tensor.

Having defined a basis of V which induces a dual basis in the dual space, the following relation holds for each element of the basis:

$$v^i(v_j) = 1 \Leftrightarrow i = j$$
$$v^i(v_j) = 0 \Leftrightarrow i \neq j$$

A tensor of order (h,k) can be defined as follows in coordinates of the basis:

$$T^{j_1,...,j_h}_{i_1,...,i_k} = T(v^{i_1},...,v^{i_k},v_{j_1},...,v_{j_h})$$

A tensor is independent of the choice of the basis and this will be clearly seen by introducing the product between tensors.

Given two different bases, they are connected by a base change matrix and its inverse matrix such that each element of a basis is given by multiplying the corresponding element of the change matrix (or of the inverse one) by the corresponding element of the other base. Two tensors can be expressed completely equivalently in one basis or the other. Given A the change of basis matrix and C the inverse matrix we have these equivalent expressions:

XII – Tensor mathematics

$$T_{i_1,\dots,i_k}^{j_1,\dots,j_h} = \sum_{l_1,\dots,l_h,m_1,\dots,m_k=1} C_{l_1}^{j_1}\dots C_{l_h}^{j_h} A_{i_1}^{m_1}\dots A_{i_k}^{m_k} \hat{T}_{m_1,\dots,m_k}^{l_1,\dots,l_h}$$

$$\hat{T}_{i_1,\dots,i_k}^{j_1,\dots,j_h} = \sum_{l_1,\dots,l_h,m_1,\dots,m_k=1} A_{l_1}^{j_1}\dots A_{l_h}^{j_h} C_{i_1}^{m_1}\dots C_{i_k}^{m_k} T_{m_1,\dots,m_k}^{l_1,\dots,l_h}$$

The h indices at the top of the tensor notation are those of contravariance as reference is made to the inverse transformation. The k indices present at the bottom in the tensor notation are those of covariance as reference is made to the direct transformation. A tensor with only down indices is called covariant, one with only up indices is called contravariant, a tensor with both up and down indices is called mixed.

For ease of notation, the so-called Einstein convention on summations is adopted at the tensor level. The convention states that, when an index occurs twice in a term of an expression, once below and once above, it is necessary to add with respect to it, unless explicitly contraindicated. For example, the scalar product is written in Einstein notation as follows:

$$\langle x, y \rangle = \sum_{i=1}^{n} x_i y_i = x_i y^i$$

The indices added according to this convention are called silent, the others are called free. A notation that contains Latin letters defines a relationship between tensors and therefore the choice of a basis of coordinates is not necessary, a notation that contains Greek letters is a relationship between the components of the tensors and therefore a choice of basis is necessary.

Two tensors of the same order can be added together or multiplied by a scalre, according to the normal rules of additivity and multiplication.

Tensor contraction is an operation that transforms a mixed tensor of order (h,k) into another mixed tensor of order (h-1,k-1). This operation is also called trace, in fact if the tensor is of order (1,1) the operation is equivalent to the calculation of the trace of the associated matrix. The contraction operation uses Einstein notation, for example like this:

$$T_{cd}^{ab} = T_{id}^{ai} = T_{d}^{a} = \sum_{i=1}^{n} T_{id}^{ai}$$

XII – Tensor mathematics

Permuting the lower or upper indices of a tensor yields another tensor of the same order. A tensor is symmetric if it does not change after any permutation of the subscripts down or up. In particular, a second order tensor is symmetric if and only if the associated matrix is symmetric. A tensor is antisymmetric if, after any permutation of the indices, it changes only in sign. In particular, a second order tensor is antisymmetric if and only if the associated matrix is antisymmetric. For an antisymmetric tensor, the values on the main diagonal of the associated matrix are all zero.

A tensor field is obtained by associating to each point of a differentiable manifold a tensor defined on the tangent space at the point. The coordinates of the tensor expressed in a map must vary in a differentiable way while the components of a tensor field with respect to different maps are connected by transformation laws expressed in partial derivatives of the coordinate functions.

The differential forms are tensor fields in which the associated tensor is antisymmetric of order (k,0). A differential form of this order can be integrated over a submanifold of dimension k.

A tensor of order (0,0) is a scalar, one of order (0,1) is a vector, one of order (1,0) is a covector. A tensor (0,2) is called a bivector while a (2,0) is a bilinear form. A tensor (3,0) is a trilinear form, as is the mixed product. A tensor (2,1) defines the vector product in three-dimensional Euclidean space.

We define Kronecker delta as a tensor of order (1,1) which represents the identity:

$$\delta^i_j = 1 \Leftrightarrow i = j$$
$$\delta^i_j = 0 \Leftrightarrow i \neq j$$

The Levi-Civita tensor is a tensor of order (n,0) and coincides with the determinant evaluated on the columns of a square matrix:

$$\varepsilon_{i_1,\dots,i_n} = \begin{cases} +1 \\ -1 \\ 0 \end{cases}$$

91

XII – Tensor mathematics

The value +1 occurs if the indices are even permutations, -1 if they are odd permutations, 0 if at least two indices coincide. In three dimensions the Levi-Civita symbol can be used to generalize the vector product:

$$\vec{a} \times \vec{b} = \sum_{i,j,k=1}^{3} \varepsilon_{ijk} a_j b_k \vec{e}_i$$

The following relations apply to the Kronecker delta:

$$\varepsilon_{ijk}\varepsilon_{imn} = \delta_{jm}\delta_{kn} - \delta_{jn}\delta_{km}$$

$$\sum_{i,j=1}^{3} \varepsilon_{ijk}\varepsilon_{ijn} = 2\delta_{kn}$$

Two tensors can be multiplied giving rise to a tensor of order equal to the sum of the orders. This operation is called the product of tensors and is indicated by:

$$T \otimes U = R$$

If T has order (h,k) and U has order (q,p), R has order (h+q,k+p). The following rules hold for covariant, contravariant, and mixed tensors:

$$A^{\mu\nu} B_{\sigma\tau} = T^{\mu\nu}_{\sigma\tau}$$

$$A^{\mu}_{\nu} B^{\tau}_{\sigma} = T^{\mu\tau}_{\nu\sigma}$$

An operation that multiplies two tensors and then contracts them is called inner product. This is possible only if the product tensor is mixed:

$$A_{\nu\mu} B^{\sigma} = T^{\sigma}_{\nu\mu} = T^{\nu}_{\nu\mu} = \sum_{\nu} T^{\nu}_{\nu\mu} = T_{\mu}$$

If there are two second-order tensors, we define a mixed product as the product equal to the inner product for two indices and to the contraction for the other two indices:

$$A_{\nu\mu} B^{\sigma\tau} = T^{\sigma\tau}_{\nu\mu} = T^{\nu\tau}_{\nu\mu} = \sum_{\nu} T^{\nu\tau}_{\nu\mu} = T^{\tau}_{\mu}$$

XII – Tensor mathematics

The covariant derivative of a tensor of order (h,k) is a tensor of order (h,k+1). If we consider the tensors (1,0) the covariant derivative of a tensor coincides with the covariant derivative of the vectors. The following properties hold, having indicated the covariant derivative with the nabla notation:

$$\nabla(\lambda_1 T_1 + \lambda_2 T_2) = \lambda_1 \nabla T_1 + \lambda_2 \nabla T_2$$
$$\nabla(T_1 \otimes T_2) = (\nabla T_1) \otimes T_2 + T_1 \otimes (\nabla T_2)$$

A map is a diffeomorphism between two open sets, one of them in an n-dimensional Euclidean space. In this open set the fields of constant coordinate vectors are defined, therefore all tensors can be written in this coordinate. In particular, the covariant derivative in any direction j is a linear combination given by:

$$\nabla_j e_i = \Gamma_{ij}^k e_k$$

Where Γ_{ij}^k are smooth functions dependent on three parameters and are called Christoffel symbols and are not tensors. The covariant derivative of a tensor field of order (2,0) is given by:

$$\nabla_k v^{ij} = \frac{\partial v^{ij}}{\partial x^k} + \Gamma_{kl}^i v^{lj} + \Gamma_{kl}^j v^{il}$$

The difference between two Christoffel symbols is a tensor which is the twist of the connection:

$$T_{ij}^k = \Gamma_{ij}^k - \Gamma_{ji}^k$$

A connection has zero torsion if and only if the Christoffel symbols are symmetrical with respect to the subscripts.
We call the following expression tensor derivative of a second order covariant tensor:

$$T_{\mu/\nu} = \frac{\partial T_\mu}{\partial x^\nu} - \Gamma_{\mu\nu}^\tau T_t$$

XII – Tensor mathematics

Using the Christoffel symbols it is therefore possible to extend the concept of tensor derivative to tensors of any second order and to tensors of any order. We call divergence of a first order tensor:

$$divT^{\mu} = T^{\mu}_{/\mu}$$

We define the contravariant derivative as:

$$\partial^{j} = g^{jl}\partial_{l}$$

The curl of a first order tensor is given by:

$$rotT^{\mu} = \varepsilon_{ijk}\partial^{j}T^{k}$$

The curl of a tensor of order (n,n) is a tensor whose columns are the curl of the rows.

The tensor g present in the contravariant derivative is the metric tensor, ie a symmetric and non-degenerate tensor field of order (0,2), defined on a differentiable manifold. The tensor defines at each point the non-degenerate dot product between the vectors of the tangent space at the point. The matrix associated with this tensor is symmetric and with a determinant other than zero.

We define the signature of a real symmetric matrix as a triad of natural numbers in which each value corresponds to the number of respectively positive, negative and null eigenvalues. In a vector space, the signature is relative to the matrix representing the dot product in that space and can be n-dimensional.

The signature of the matrix associated with the metric tensor is the same for each point if the differentiable manifold is connected. If the signature is of the type (n,0), the scalar product is everywhere positive definite: a metric is induced on the manifold which is called Riemannian. When the scalar product is not positive definite, the manifold is called pseudo-Riemannian.

If the metric tensor is associated with the identity matrix we have a Euclidean space with Euclidean metric. In spherical coordinates the metric tensor is given by:

$$g = \begin{bmatrix} 1 & 0 \\ 0 & \sin^2 \vartheta \end{bmatrix}$$

The metric tensor is associated with a similar tensor of order $(0,2)$ called the conjugate metric tensor defined by a matrix which is the inverse of that relating to the metric tensor. The metric tensor can be used to transform vectors into covectors and vice versa, as follows:

$$T_\nu = g_{\nu\mu} T^\mu$$
$$T^\mu = g^{\mu\nu} T_\nu$$

We define Riemannian manifold as a differentiable manifold having a positive definite metric tensor which therefore represents a scalar product (positive definite) on the tangent space of each point of the manifold. The angle between two tangent vectors belonging to the tangent space is equal to:

$$\vartheta = \arccos \frac{g(\alpha'(0), \beta'(0))}{\sqrt{g(\alpha'(0), \alpha'(0)) \cdot g(\beta'(0), \beta'(0))}}$$

The length of a differentiable curve in the Riemannian manifold is given by:

$$L(\Gamma) = \int_a^b \|\Gamma'(t)\| dt$$

The distance between two points of the manifold defines a structure of metric space and is as follows:

$$d(x, y) = \inf \{L(\alpha)\}$$

An oriented Riemannian manifold has a shape that expresses volume. On tangent space, this form is the only antisymmetric tensor of order $(n,0)$ defined on any positive orthonormal basis:

$$\omega(e_1, ..., e_n) = 1$$

95

XII – Tensor mathematics

In a card the form that expresses the volume is given by:

$$\omega = \sqrt{\det g}\, dx^1 \wedge ... \wedge dx^n$$

Volume is the simple integral of this form over a computational domain.

A compact Riemannian manifold is always complete, that is, it is a metric space in which all Cauchy sequences converge to an element of the space. More generally, the Hopf-Rinow theorem holds according to which a Riemannian manifold connected by arcs is a complete metric space, has closed and bounded subsets which are compact and every geodesic can be prolonged indefinitely. The n-dimensional Euclidean space R is therefore complete, while if one removes a point from any Riemannian manifold, one obtains one that is not complete. Completeness depends on the metric tensor, i.e. a same Riemannian manifold can be complete or not based on the definition of the metric.

We call the curvature of the Riemannian manifold the tendency to depart from the Euclidean metric. According to the egregium theorem, the Gaussian curvature of a surface is an intrinsic quantity, i.e. it does not depend on isometric transformations. The Gaussian curvature of a surface is the determinant of the Hessian, while for higher order Riemannian manifolds the curvature is given by a tensor, called the Riemann tensor.

Considering a differentiable manifold endowed with a connection, the Riemann tensor of order (1,3) is the tensor which satisfies this equality:

$$R(X,Y)Z = \nabla_X \nabla_Y Z - \nabla_Y \nabla_X Z - \nabla_{[X,Y]}Z$$

Where X, Y, Z are vector fields. If Schwarz's theorem holds, such as in a Euclidean space, the first two terms cancel. The third term contains the Lie brackets that will be introduced later in this textbook when discussing advanced algebra. Based on the Christoffel symbols, the Riemann tensor can be expressed as follows:

$$R^\sigma_{\mu\nu\kappa} = \frac{\partial \Gamma^\sigma_{\mu\nu}}{\partial x^\kappa} - \frac{\partial \Gamma^\sigma_{\mu\kappa}}{\partial x^\nu} + \Gamma^\lambda_{\mu\nu}\Gamma^\sigma_{\kappa\lambda} - \Gamma^\lambda_{\mu\kappa}\Gamma^\sigma_{\nu\lambda}$$

XII – Tensor mathematics

The Riemann tensor is antisymmetric with respect to the exchange of the first two or the last two indices and symmetric with respect to the exchange of the two pairs of indices. Moreover, in the absence of torsion, Bianchi's first and second identities hold:

$$R^{\rho}_{\sigma\mu\nu} + R^{\rho}_{\nu\sigma\mu} + R^{\rho}_{\mu\nu\sigma} = 0$$

$$\nabla_{\lambda} R_{\rho\sigma\mu\nu} + \nabla_{\rho} R_{\sigma\lambda\mu\nu} + \nabla_{\sigma} R_{\lambda\rho\mu\nu} = 0$$

The Riemann tensor of a surface is given by:

$$R_{\rho\sigma\mu\nu} = K(g_{\rho\mu}g_{\sigma\nu} - g_{\rho\nu}g_{\sigma\mu})$$

Where K is the Gaussian curvature. The Riemann tensor of a Euclidean space is zero; a Riemannian manifold with zero Riemann tensor is said to be flat. By measuring the curvature of a Riemannian manifold, the Riemann tensor is decisive for the calculation of geodesics. By contracting the Riemann tensor, we get the Ricci tensor:

$$R_{ij} = R^{k}_{ikj}$$

From Bianchi's first identity it follows that the Ricci tensor is symmetric and of order (0,2). A manifold in which the Ricci tensor is a multiple of the metric tensor is called an Einstein manifold. The trace of the Ricci tensor is the scalar curvature R. The Einstein tensor is defined as follows:

$$G_{ij} = R_{ij} - \frac{R}{2}g_{ij}$$

From Bianchi's second identity we have:

$$\nabla_{i} G^{ij} = 0$$

The only torsion-free connection that preserves the metric on a Riemannian manifold is called the Levi-Civita connection. For such a connection, the Christoffel symbols are symmetric in the lower indices and the covariant derivative of the metric tensor is zero. Therefore,

XII – Tensor mathematics

given a Riemannian manifold, the corresponding Levi-Civita connection exists and is unique.

We can introduce the concept of tensor product between vector spaces as a vector space with a bilinear map for which there is a unique homomorphism that expresses this operation and is denoted as follows:

$$U \cong V \otimes W$$

The following properties of the tensor product between vector spaces hold:

$$(U \otimes V) \otimes W \cong U \otimes (V \otimes W)$$
$$V \otimes W \cong W \otimes V$$
$$U \otimes (V \oplus W) \cong (U \oplus V) \otimes (U \oplus W)$$
$$k \otimes V \cong V$$
$$k^n \otimes V \cong V^n$$
$$k^n \otimes k^m \cong k^{nm}$$

We define a bundle as a continuous surjective function between topological spaces which, locally, is a product. In particular, given a topological space, called fiber, every point belonging to the topological space related by the bundle to the fiber has an open neighborhood, called base, such that the counterimage, called projection, is homeomorphic to a product between the base and the fiber.

A bundle is smooth if it is defined on differentiable manifolds, in which case the projection, the base and the fiber are differentiable manifolds and the bundle is a differentiable function.

If the product is the tensor one we have a tensor bundle of order (m,n) where minus are the dimensions of the vector spaces to be tensorily multiplied.

In a tensor bundle we can define local coordinates as done for tensors, while the Christoffel symbols are the coefficients of the connection that relates the set of sections of the bundle to the set given by the tensor product between the vector spaces that define the bundle.

Tensor mathematics is of particular importance in physics, as many physical quantities are tensors (for example quantities that express mechanical, electrical, optical and magnetic characteristics of materials).

XII – Tensor mathematics

Furthermore, tensor mathematics is the basis for understanding the general theory of relativity.

XII – Tensor mathematics

XIII – INTEGRAL CALCULUS FOR FUNCTIONS OF SEVERAL VARIABLES

Given a function of several real variables, it is possible to define the multiple integral according to Riemann, ie the integral carried out in each of its variables. The theorems of the integral mean and the weighted mean as well as the properties of monotonicity, additivity and linearity always hold. The notation is the same except to make explicit the writing for double and triple integrals:

$$\iint_T f(x, y)dxdy$$
$$\iiint_S f(x, y, z)dxdydz$$

Similarly, improper integrals maintain their properties and the methods of solving a multiple integral are the same, almost always accompanied by attempts to reduce the multiple integral into n different and successive integrations with respect to the n single variables. The reduction formulas are based on the assumption of a corollary of Fubini's theorem according to which if the integrand function, for example of two real variables, can be expressed as the product of two functions defined on a single variable, then also the integral double can be reduced to the product of two simple integrals:

$$f(x, y) = h(x)g(y) \Rightarrow \iint_T f(x, y)d(x, y) = \iint_T h(x)g(y)dxdy = \left(\int_A h(x)dx\right)\left(\int_B g(y)dy\right)$$

Where the set T is given by the Cartesian product of the sets A and B. This corollary guarantees this result for functions in which the integral of the absolute value converges; Tonelli's theorem guarantees the same result for positive functions. Such a reduction is also possible if the integrand function is continuous and the integration set is bounded.
If a change of variable is made in the calculation of multiple integrals, the following relation holds:

$$\int_A f(x_1,...,x_n)d(x_1,...,x_n) = \int_B f(g(y_1,...,y_n))\left|\det(J_g(y))\right|d(y_1,....y_n)$$

XIII – Integral calculus for functions of several variables

The determinant of the Jacobian matrix relating to the function after the change of variable appears in the formula; in polar and cylindrical coordinates this determinant is equal to r, in three-dimensional spherical coordinates it is equal to $r^2 \sin \vartheta$.

A surface integral is defined by a double integral. A surface can be parameterized like this:

$$S(u,v) = (x(u,v), y(u,v), z(u,v))$$

To each point we can associate the normal vector given by:

$$\vec{N}(u,v) = \frac{\partial(y,z)}{\partial(u,v)}\vec{e}_1 + \frac{\partial(z,x)}{\partial(u,v)}\vec{e}_2 + \frac{\partial(x,y)}{\partial(u,v)}\vec{e}_3$$

We define the surface integral of a function f on the surface S in a domain D as follows:

$$\int_S f dV = \int_D f(S(u,v)) |N(u,v)| du dv$$

If f=1 the surface integral represents the surface area. If f can be expressed as a vector field we have the following expression:

$$\int_S \vec{F} \cdot d\vec{S} = \int_S (\vec{F} \cdot \vec{n}) dS$$

where n is the normal vector to the surface. If this integral is zero we say that the vector field is solenoidal and we can find another vector field, called vector potential, such that:

$$\nabla \times \vec{A} = \vec{F}$$

Similarly an integral of volume is given by a triple integral and if the function f=1, this integral returns precisely the volume of the region of space considered:

$$vol(D) = \iiint_D dx dy dz$$

XIII – Integral calculus for functions of several variables

Given a curve parametrized by a smooth function and a piecewise smooth plane curve that is simple and closed, the curl theorem holds for a vector field:

$$\oint_\Gamma \vec{F}d\Gamma = \iint_S \nabla \times \vec{F}dS$$

This theorem relates the line integral to the surface integral. The theorem is a generalization of the fundamental theorem of integral calculus and is related to the definitions of conservatism and irrotality of a vector field.

A special case of the rotor theorem is Green's theorem. Given a piecewise regular closed simple curve which is the boundary of a surface and given two real functions of two real variables which have continuous partial derivatives on an open set which contains the surface then we have that:

$$\oint_{\partial S}(f(x,y)dx + g(x,y)dy) = \iint_S \left(\frac{\partial g(x,y)}{\partial x} - \frac{\partial f(x,y)}{\partial y} \right)dxdy$$

This theorem is therefore the curl theorem in the two-dimensional case. Green's theorem is also the two-dimensional special case of another theorem, known as the divergence theorem.

Given a compact set V bounded by a smooth surface and a continuously differentiable vector field defined in a neighborhood of the compact set, the divergence theorem states that:

$$\int_V \nabla \cdot \vec{F}dv = \oint_{\partial V} \vec{F} \cdot d\vec{s} = \oint_{\partial V} \vec{F} \cdot \vec{n}dS$$

The flux of the vector field through the closed surface coincides with the integral of the divergence in the volume. If the vector field has a radial density distribution, the divergence theorem is called the flux theorem or Gauss's theorem and the following integral and differential expressions are obtained:

$$\int_V (\nabla \cdot \vec{F} - \sigma(\vec{r}))dv = 0$$

$$\nabla \cdot \vec{F} = \sigma(\vec{r})$$

XIII – Integral calculus for functions of several variables

The divergence theorem has two corollaries expressed by the two Green identities.
Given two scalar functions, one differentiable twice with continuity and the other differentiable once with continuity such that a vector field can be expressed as:

$$\vec{F} = \psi \nabla \varphi$$

Then Green's first identity states that:

$$\int_{V} (\psi \nabla^{2} \varphi + \nabla \varphi \cdot \nabla \psi) dV = \oint_{\partial V} \psi (\nabla \varphi \cdot \vec{n}) dS$$

If instead the vector field is expressed as follows:

$$\vec{F} = \psi \varepsilon \nabla \varphi - \varphi \varepsilon \nabla \psi$$

Green's second identity is as follows:

$$\int_{V} \left[\psi \nabla \cdot (\varepsilon \nabla \varphi) - \varphi \nabla \cdot (\varepsilon \nabla \psi) \right] dV = \oint_{\partial V} \varepsilon \left(\psi \frac{\partial \varphi}{\partial n} - \varphi \frac{\partial \psi}{\partial n} \right) dS$$

The theorem that generalizes both the divergence and the curl and Green's theorems is Stokes' theorem. According to this theorem, given a form of order (n-1) with compact support on a differentiable manifold of dimension n endowed with a frontier then it holds:

$$\int_{\Omega} d\omega = \oint_{\partial \Omega} \omega$$

where $d\omega$ is the exterior derivative. From this relation it necessarily follows that if the variety is closed, the integral is zero. The curl theorem is the application of Stokes' theorem to a form of order one, in which the exterior derivative is precisely represented by the curl. In the case of a continuously differentiable vector field we fall back on the divergence theorem. In the case of a form of order one defined on a manifold of dimension one, Stokes' theorem coincides with the gradient theorem.

XIV – DEVELOPMENTS IN SERIES

Before introducing series of functions it is necessary to return to the convergence criteria for numerical series which define sufficient conditions for the convergence of a series.

For series with concordant terms, several criteria apply.

The first criterion of the comparison states that given two series with non-negative terms, if the majority converges the minor also converges, while if the minor diverges, the major also does so. The second criterion of the comparison brings in the asymptotic comparison. Indeed, from two series with positive terms, if one is convergent and the limit of the ratio between the other series and this one exists and is finite, then the other series is also convergent. Similarly, if one series is divergent and the limit of the ratio between the other series and the latter is positive, then the other series is also divergent.

From these criteria of comparison others derive as corollaries such as for example the criterion of the root. Given a series with non-negative terms and for which the limit of the nth root of the nth element exists, then the series converges if this limit is less than one.

The ratio criterion states that given a series with positive terms and for which the limit of the ratio between the last term and the penultimate exists, then the series converges if this limit is less than one.

In doing so it is also possible to evaluate the remainder, ie the error that is committed by calculating the sum of a series stopping at the n-th term.

$$\sum_{n=0}^{\infty} a_n = \sum_{n=0}^{N} a_n + R_N$$

Using the previous criteria, the remainder can be increased by the following expressions:

$$R_N < C \frac{k^{N+1}}{1-k}$$

$$R_N < \frac{a_{N+1}}{1-k'}$$

Raabe's criterion states that if there is a finite limit of this quantity:

XIV – Developments in series

$$\lim_{n\to\infty} n\left(\frac{a_n}{a_{n+1}} - 1\right) = l$$

The series converges if this limit is less than one.

For series with discordant terms, a sufficient condition for convergence is given by absolute convergence, ie by the convergence of the series calculated by adding the modules of the single terms. A series with discordant terms is said to have terms with alternating sign if two consecutive terms always have opposite signs. For these series, the convergence criterion of Leibnitz is valid according to which a series of terms with alternating sign converges if the sequence of absolute values of the terms is definitively positive, decreasing and tending to zero. Furthermore, partial sums of even order and of odd order are monotone and tend to the same values as the series tends.

Dirichlet's convergence criterion states that given two series with discordant terms, one monotonously tends to zero and the other is bounded, then the series given by the sum of the products of the individual terms of the two previous series converges. Dirichlet's criterion generalizes that of Leibnitz.

This criterion makes use of the addition by parts or a formula similar to that of integration by parts to evaluate the series of products.

A sequence of functions is a sequence whose terms are functions. Given a sequence of functions and a metric space, it is said to converge pointwise if it happens for every point belonging to the domain:

$$\lim_{n\to\infty} f_n(x) = f(x)$$

Define the following sequence:

$$a_n = \sup_{x\in D} |f_n(x) - f(x)|$$

If it is well defined and the limit of the nth term is zero, the sequence is said to converge uniformly. If the sequence converges uniformly, the following properties hold: the limit of a sequence of continuous functions is a continuous function just as the limit of differentiable or integrable functions is a derivable or integrable function or the limit of

XIV – Developments in series

limited or uniformly continuous functions. Furthermore, the limit of the integrals of a sequence of functions is the integral of the limit just as the limit of the derivatives of a sequence of functions is the derivative of the limit, i.e. it is possible to exchange the signs of limit, sum, integral and derivative if there is uniform convergence.

Dini's lemma states that if a sequence of functions converges punctually and monotonously and the functions are continuous in a compact set, then the sequence converges uniformly.

Given a sequence of functions defined in an open set, it converges both pointwise and uniformly if and only if Cauchy's convergence criterion holds.

$$\forall \varepsilon > 0, \exists v \varepsilon N : \forall x \in (a,b), \forall n,m > v \left| \left| f_n(x) - f_m(x) \right| \right| < \varepsilon$$

Similarly to what was done for numerical series, it is possible to define series of functions. A series of functions pointwise converges to a function if the corresponding numerical series converges. The same goes for uniform convergence and absolute convergence.

A series of functions converges totally if the following relation holds:

$$\sum \sup_{x \in X} \left| f_n(x) \right| < \infty$$

If a series of functions converges totally, then it also converges uniformly, absolutely and pointwise. Among all the examples of series of functions we will make explicit the power series, the Taylor series and the Fourier series. In all these cases we speak of the series expansion of a function.

A power series is a particular series of functions that can be expressed with this relation:

$$f(x) = \sum_{n=0}^{\infty} a_n (x-c)^n$$

These series are generalizations of polynomials and the coefficients can assume real or complex values. The coefficient c is called the center of the series. A power series converges for some value of the variable x. There is a value, called radius of convergence, such that the series converges if this condition is met:

XIV – Developments in series

$$|x-c| < R$$

The radius of convergence is calculated by the Cauchy-Hadamard formula:

$$R = \liminf_{n\to\infty} \frac{1}{\sqrt[n]{|a_n|}}$$

If the limit exists and is finite, i.e. if the radius of convergence is not infinite, then the previous formula can be simplified according to D'Alembert's formula:

$$R = \lim_{n\to\infty} \left| \frac{a_n}{a_{n+1}} \right|$$

Where the series converges, absolute convergence also occurs, while total and uniform convergence occur for each compact subset.
Abel's theorem states that if the power series converges at a point on the frontier then the series is continuous at that point. Furthermore, if the power series converges punctually at a point then it converges uniformly in a compact contained within the interval between the magnitude of that point's value. Abel's theorem allows an estimate of the radius of convergence: in fact, given a series centered in one point and converging in another point, the radius of convergence is greater than or equal to the module of the distance between the two points.
Given two power series, addition and subtraction are done by adding or subtracting their respective coefficients. The multiplication of two power series is defined as follows:

$$(f \cdot g)(x) = \left(\sum_{n=0}^{\infty} a_n (x-c)^n \right) \cdot \left(\sum_{n=0}^{\infty} b_n (x-c)^n \right) = \sum_{n=0}^{\infty} \left(\sum_{i=0}^{n} a_i b_{n-i} \right)(x-c)^n$$

This product is called the Cauchy product or convolution. The power series given by the addition, subtraction or convolution of two power series has a radius of convergence greater than or equal to the minimum of the radii of convergence of the two starting series. The derivative and integral of a power series are given by:

$$f'(x) = \sum_{n=0}^{\infty} a_{n+1}(n+1)(x-c)^n$$

$$\int f(x)dx = \sum_{n=0}^{\infty} \frac{a_n(x-c)^{n+1}}{n+1} + C$$

And they have the same radius of convergence as f(x).
A function defined on an open subset of R is analytic if it can be represented locally as a power series. We will analyze the analytic functions more deeply by speaking of complex analysis. Power series of functions of several variables can easily be reduced to what has been said for power series of functions of one variable.
The Taylor series is a power series of an infinitely differentiable function defined in an open set. The Taylor series calculated at any point at any point is given by:

$$\sum_{n=0}^{\infty} \frac{f^{(n)}(a)}{n!}(x-a)^n$$

If the point is zero, the series is called a Maclaurin series. If the series is truncated at the nth order, it is called a Taylor polynomial. A function can be expressed as the sum of the Taylor polynomial and a remainder that is an infinitesimal of higher order than the nth degree.
The remainder can be expressed in Peano's form, with the indication of o-small compared to the nth degree or in Lagrange's form, in which if the function is n+1 times differentiable around a point, the remainder it is given by:

$$R_n(x) = \frac{f^{(n+1)}(\xi)}{(n+1)!}(x-x_0)^{n+1}$$

Through the interpretation of the remainder according to Lagrange, we see that Taylor's formula generalizes Lagrange's theorem. Through the interpretation according to Peano it is instead possible to resolve many forms of indeterminacy in the calculation of the limits, above all when the point in which the series is calculated is zero.

XIV – Developments in series

If we consider a function G(t) continuous, differentiable and with non-zero derivative, then the remainder can also be expressed in the Cauchy form:

$$R_n(x) = \frac{f^{(n+1)}(\xi)}{n!}(x-\xi)^n \frac{G(x)-G(a)}{G'(\xi)}$$

This form generalizes Cauchy's theorem. Finally, the remainder can be expressed in integral form, generalizing the fundamental theorem of integral calculus. If the nth derivative is absolutely continuous, the remainder is given by:

$$R_n(x) = \int_a^x \frac{f^{(n+1)}(t)}{n!}(x-t)^n \, dt$$

For functions of several variables, Taylor's formula remains valid unless we remember the use of multi-indexes. If the function is analytic, the expansion in Taylor series allows term-by-term differentiation and integration. The Maclaurin series expansions of the principal functions are as follows:

$$e^x = \sum_{n=0}^{\infty} \frac{x^n}{n!}$$

$$\ln(1+x) = \sum_{n=1}^{\infty} \frac{(-1)^{n+1} x^n}{n}$$

$$\sin x = \sum_{n=0}^{\infty} \frac{(-1)^n x^{2n+1}}{(2n+1)!}$$

$$\cos x = \sum_{n=0}^{\infty} \frac{(-1)^n x^{2n}}{(2n)!}$$

$$\sinh x = \sum_{n=0}^{\infty} \frac{x^{2n+1}}{(2n+1)!}$$

$$\cosh x = \sum_{n=0}^{\infty} \frac{x^{2n}}{(2n)!}$$

XIV – Developments in series

Through the Maclaurin series expansions it is also possible to obtain both the geometric series and the binomial expansion.

The expansion in Fourier series is part of the so-called Fourier analysis or harmonic analysis which includes various parts of mathematics. The Fourier series is a linear combination of fundamental sinusoidal functions to express a periodic starting function. A Fourier series can be expressed as follows:

$$f(x) = \frac{a_0}{2} + \sum_{n=1}^{\infty} [a_n \cos(nx) + b_n \sin(nx)] = \sum_{n=-\infty}^{\infty} c_n e^{inx}$$

This series is expressed in rectangular form. One can express the Fourier series in complex form and in polar form, as follows:

$$f(x) = \sum_{n=-\infty}^{\infty} \gamma_n e^{\frac{i2\pi nx}{T}}$$

$$f(x) = c_0 + 2\sum_{n=1}^{\infty} c_n \cos\left(\frac{2\pi nx}{T} + \phi_n\right)$$

The Fourier series of a continuous function defined on the unit circle does not always converge to the function itself. To correctly define convergence and the properties of Fourier series, some fundamentals of functional analysis are needed, which we will find later in this manual.

Through the Fourier series it is also possible to develop functions that are not periodic in nature, such as the identity function f(x)=x, it is enough to make these functions periodic by limiting them to an interval which then repeats itself periodically.

The expansions in Fourier series also account for the denomination between even and odd functions. An even function is a function that can be expressed, in the formalism of Fourier series, only as a linear combination of cosines; on the other hand, an odd function as a linear combination of sines.

XIV – Developments in series

XV – COMPLEX ANALYSIS

If the function considered in mathematical analysis is a complex variable and not real, we speak of complex analysis. Given an open subset of the complex plane, a function is differentiable in the complex sense if such a limit exists:

$$f'(z_0) = \lim_{z \to z_0} \frac{f(z) - f(z_0)}{z - z_0}$$

This limit means that, for each sequence of complex numbers that converge to a given point, the limit of the incremental ratio must tend to the same value. A function is said to be holomorphic in a set if it is differentiable in the complex sense at every point in the set. A function is differentiable in the complex sense if it is differentiable and if this relation holds:

$$\lim_{\Delta z \to 0} \frac{f(z_0 + \Delta z) - f(z_0) - f'(z_0)\Delta z}{\Delta z} = 0$$

Continuity in the complex sense is defined in the same way as for the case of real functions. It is possible to relate the differentiability between complex functions and real functions simply by recalling the Cartesian form of complex numbers:

$$f(z) = u(x, y) + iv(x, y)$$

A function is holomorphic if and only if it satisfies the Cauchy-Riemann equations:

$$\frac{\partial u}{\partial x} = \frac{\partial v}{\partial y}$$
$$\frac{\partial u}{\partial y} = -\frac{\partial v}{\partial x}$$

XV – Complex analysis

The components u(x,y) and v(x,y) of a holomorphic function are harmonic functions. A holomorphic function is differentiable infinite times, while the Wirtinger derivative of a holomorphic function is zero:

$$\frac{\partial f(z)}{\partial \overline{z}} = 0$$

A complex function of several variables is holomorphic if and only if it can be developed as a convergent power series (this condition is more stringent than the Cauchy-Riemann equations alone for complex functions of one variable) i.e. every holomorphic function is analytic.

By Liouville's theorem, every bounded holomorphic function defined on the entire complex plane is a constant.

Furthermore, each analytic function of real variable extends uniquely to a holomorphic function. This procedure is called analytic extension and can be applied to functions such as the exponential and the majority of trigonometric functions. On the other hand, we speak of analytic continuation when it is possible to extend the domain of definition of a holomorphic function, maintaining the same starting holomorphic function in the original domain. Typically, analytic continuation is not a one-time operation.

A holomorphic function whose derivative is always non-zero is a conformal map. We define a conformal map as a function which preserves the angles and their orientation, but not necessarily the dimensions.

Anti-holomorphic functions are those complex functions that are holomorphic with respect to the complex conjugate of the argument. A function that is both holomorphic and anti-holomorphic is constant. An anti-holomorphic function preserves the angles, but not their orientation, and is therefore not a conformal map.

A Riemann surface is a connected topological manifold, Hausdorff, two-dimensional and has a complex structure such that the function describing the manifold is holomorphic. For example, every open subset of the complex plane is a Riemann surface. A Riemann surface is orientable, as it is described by a holomorphic function which is a conformal map.

A Riemann sphere is a Riemann surface that is obtained by adding a point at infinity to the complex plane. In essence it is the generalization of the projective line in the complex plane. A Riemann sphere is the simplest compact Riemann surface.

XV – Complex analysis

The Riemann uniformization theorem states that a Riemann surface admits a Riemannian metric with constant curvature which induces the same conformal structure given by the original structure of the Riemann surface. The value of the curvature can be 1, 0 or -1 and we speak, respectively, of elliptical, flat or hyperbolic metric. Only if the metric is flat can it be scaled with a multiplicative factor, while in all other cases the metric is unique.

A biolomorphism is a holomorphic function which is injective, surjective and whose inverse is holomorphic. The biolomorphism relation generalizes the isomorphism relation for the case of complex analysis. A biolomorphism between Riemann surfaces is given by a bijective holomorphic function.

If the Riemann surface is simply connected, then the Riemann uniformization theorem reduces to the Riemann map theorem which states that the surface is biolomorphic to one of the following models: the Poincaré disk, the complex plane or the Riemann, whose curvatures are -1.0 and 1. In all these cases, biolomorphisms are also isometries. The biolomorphisms of the Riemann sphere are the Mobius transformations, those of the complex plane are the translations, those of the Poincaré disk are the so-called Fuchsian groups.

We define an integer function as a function that is holomorphic on all points of the complex plane. Every integer function can be expressed by a Taylor series expansion. The simplest integer functions are polynomials, the exponential function, trigonometric functions such as sine and cosine, and hyperbolic functions, such as hyperbolic sine and cosine. The sum, difference, product, derivation, and composition of integer functions are integer functions, whereas inverse functions (eg, logarithm, square root, arcsine) or quotients of integer functions are usually not.

Integer functions, as well as complex functions, can be polydrome, i.e. have multiple values, or monodrome. The polydromy of complex functions derives from the very nature of complex numbers; in fact if the power function is monodrome, the nth root is polydrome (as is the root of unity) and the complex logarithm is also polydrome.

We call zero of a holomorphic function a complex number such that the function vanishes for that value. It is called simple zero, or zero of multiplicity one, if it happens that:

$$f(z) = (z-a)g(z)\big|_{z=a} = 0 : g(a) \neq 0$$

Where g(z) is a holomorphic function. The multiplicity of a zero is that positive integer n such that:

$$f(z) = (z-a)^n g(z)\big|_{z=a} = 0 : g(a) \neq 0$$

The fundamental theorem of algebra guarantees that every non-constant polynomial with complex coefficients has at least one zero in the complex plane. Considering the multiplicity of zeros, every polynomial of degree n has n zeros in the complex plane. A holomorphic function has isolated zeros, i.e. there is a neighborhood of each zero that does not contain other zeros.

A complex function has an isolated singularity in a point if there is a neighborhood of the point for which the function is holomorphic in the neighborhood but not in the point. A singularity is said to be eliminated if such a limit exists:

$$\lim_{z \to z_0} f(z) = l$$

This relation is equivalent to saying that the modulus of f(z) is bounded in a neighborhood of the point or that the function extends to a holomorphic function in the whole open space. A singularity can be eliminated precisely because the method of analytic continuation can be used to eliminate it.

A singularity is called a pole if there exists a positive natural number such that the limit exists:

$$\lim_{z \to z_0} (z - z_0)^n f(z) = l$$

This limit must be non-zero. The number n is the multiplicity of the pole and if it is equal to one, the pole is called simple. This relation is equivalent to saying that the module of f(z) is infinite at the point or that the function given by the reciprocal of f(z) has a singularity at the point that can be eliminated.

A singularity that is not removable or a pole is called an essential singularity. In this case, the modulus of f(z) has no limit at the considered point. For essential singularities, Picard's theorem is valid according to which, given a holomorphic function with essential singularity in a point, the function assumes all complex values in any neighborhood of the point except at most one. Furthermore, the Casorati-Weierstrass theorem also holds according to which, under the same assumptions of Picard's theorem, the function computed in the neighborhood of the essential singularity, with the exception of the singularity point, is dense in the complex plane.

An integer function has a singularity at infinity which is classifiable according to what has just been reported. Liouville's theorem states that an integer function having infinitely eliminating singularities is a constant.

A meromorphic function is defined as a function which is holomorphic on an open set of the complex plane with the exception of a set of isolated points, which are the poles. Every function expressed as a ratio between two holomorphic functions is meromorphic on the complex plane and the poles are the zeros of the denominator. A meromorphic function is given by a holomorphic function whose codomain is the Riemann sphere.

Polydrome functions, on the other hand, have non-isolated singularities called branch points. A branch point is of order n, if making n+1 revolutions in the same direction around the point, the function always assumes the same initial value; on the other hand, it is of infinite order if the function never returns to the same initial value.

For a polydrome function it is possible to define inverse monodrome functions. On the basis of the choice of this inverse function, we speak of a branch of the inverse, one of which is taken, by convention, as the main branch and the values assumed by the polydrome function in that branch are called main values.

The exponential function of complex argument is periodic of period equal to $2\pi i$ and is a holomorphic function.

The complex logarithm is always defined in the complex plane, except for the zero argument. Using Cartesian notation, it can be written as:

$$\ln z = \ln|z| + i \arg z$$

Since arg(z) contains infinitely many values of period equal to 2π, the logarithm function is polydrome. The principal value of the complex logarithm is the value it assumes when:

$$-\pi < \arg z < \pi$$

XV – Complex analysis

We call complex integration the integral evaluated along a rectifiable curve, ie a curve in which the length is given by the upper bound of the sums of the infinitesimal polygonal distances. If the curve is continuously differentiable, then the complex integral reduces to the computation of an integral of real function. The complex integration curve can also be closed. From the Cauchy-Riemann equations, it follows that the curl of a vector field corresponding to the conjugate of a holomorphic function is null.

For complex integration, Cauchy's integral theorem holds according to which, given a holomorphic function defined on a simply connected domain, for every piecewise regular closed curve we have that:

$$\oint_{\partial S} f(z)dz = 0$$

As a corollary, the integral over a curve depends only on the extrema; furthermore the holomorphic function admits a primitive. If the domains are multiconnected, the Cauchy integral theorem can be applied separately for the single connections and then summed.

Given a holomorphic function in a simply connected domain and a closed simple curve traveled counterclockwise and called z at any point within the region enclosed by the curve then the Cauchy integral formula holds:

$$f(z) = \frac{1}{2\pi i} \oint_\gamma \frac{f(z')}{z' - z} dz'$$

It can be seen that a complex function that can be expressed with this integral formula and that is continuous is necessarily holomorphic. This result is known as Morera's theorem.

From this formula, we obtain the expression for the nth derivative of a holomorphic function:

$$f^{(n)}(z) = \frac{n!}{2\pi i} \oint_\gamma \frac{f(z')}{(z' - z)^{n+1}} dz'$$

Furthermore, the mean theorem is obtained. An analytic function in a point coincides with the mean of the values assumed by the function on the points of a circle of radius re centered in the point:

XV – Complex analysis

$$f(z) = \frac{1}{2\pi} \int_0^{2\pi} f(z + re^{i\vartheta})d\vartheta$$

If f(z) is a function limited by a value M, called L the length of the curve and D the minimum distance between a point and the curve, the following increases hold:

$$|f(z)| \le \frac{ML}{2\pi D}$$

$$|f^{(n)}(z)| \le \frac{n!ML}{2\pi D^{n+1}}$$

From Cauchy's integral formula also derives the maximum modulus theorem according to which a holomorphic and continuous function on a curve has the maximum modulus value not within the domain, but on the curve itself.

Given an isolated singularity and a holomorphic function, the integral of the function calculated along a circle of radius re-centered in the isolated singularity is defined as residual:

$$\mathrm{Re}\, s(f, z_0) = \frac{1}{2\pi i} \oint_{\gamma_r} f(z)dz$$

The radius is chosen to contain a single isolated singularity. The residue theorem states that given a holomorphic function having n isolated singularities and a closed simple curve, the line integral holds:

$$\oint_\gamma f(z)dz = 2\pi i \sum_{k=1}^{n} I(\gamma, z_k)\,\mathrm{Re}\, s(f, z_k)$$

The formula contains the curve winding index, ie the number of times the curve wraps around the isolated singularity. This index is positive if the curve rotates counterclockwise, negative if vice versa. Thus, complex integration depends both on the path of integration and on the direction of integration.

If the singularity can be eliminated then the residue is zero, if instead the singularity is a pole of order k, the residue is:

XV – Complex analysis

$$\operatorname{Re} s(z_0) = \frac{1}{(k-1)!} \frac{d^{k-1}}{dz^{k-1}} \left[(z-z_0)^k \cdot f(z) \right]_{z=z_0}$$

A holomorphic function defined in a neighborhood of infinity has a residue at infinity:

$$\operatorname{Re} s_\infty f(z) = -\frac{1}{2\pi i} \oint_\gamma f(z)dz$$

The implication of this formula is that the sum of the residuals is zero:

$$\sum_{i=1}^{k} \operatorname{Re} s(f, z_i) + \operatorname{Re} s_\infty f(z) = 0$$

Jordan's lemma states that, given a continuous complex function on the entire complex plane and an arc of circumference having its center at the origin of the plane, with radius R, and extended between two angles between 0 and 180°, the following implication holds :

$$\lim_{R \to +\infty} \max_{\vartheta \in [\vartheta_1; \vartheta_2]} \left| f(R \cdot e^{i\vartheta}) \right| = 0 \Rightarrow \exists \omega \in R, \omega > 0 : \lim_{R \to +\infty} \int_{\gamma_R} f(z)e^{i\omega z} dz = 0$$

It is possible to extend Jordan's lemma also for curvilinear abscissas with angles between 180° and 360°. Where there is the presence of isolated singularities, this lemma can be applied combined with the theorem of residues, decomposing the curvilinear abscissa as the sum of integrals along a curve to which this lemma applies and of integrals along a curve to which the theorem applies of the residues.
Jordan's lemma is completed by the great circle lemma according to which, given an unlimited open set of the complex plane and a holomorphic function in this open set, we have:

$$\lim_{|z| \to +\infty} zf(z) = 0 \Rightarrow \lim_{R \to +\infty} \int_{\gamma_R \cap \Omega} f(z)dz = 0$$

Where R is the radius of a semicircle that creates a closed curve around a pole. Finally, there are also the two lemmas of the small circle. The

XV – Complex analysis

first of them states that, under the same hypotheses of the lemma of the large circle, it holds:

$$\lim_{z \to z_0}(z - z_0)f(z) = 0 \Rightarrow \lim_{r \to 0}\int_{\gamma_r} f(z)dz = 0$$

From this lemma it follows that a continuous complex function in an open set and having isolated singularity of type that can be eliminated has zero integral around this singularity.

The second lemma states that if the function has a simple pole then:

$$\int_{\gamma_r} f(z)dz = i(\phi_2 - \phi_1)\operatorname{Re} s(f, z_0)$$

The Euler gamma function is defined as:

$$\Gamma(z) = \int_0^{+\infty} t^{z-1}e^{-t}dt$$

If Re(z)>0 then this integral converges absolutely. It is possible to define this function for all complex numbers through analytic continuation, provided that Re(z) is negative and not integer. The following properties hold:

$$\Gamma(z+1) = z\Gamma(z) \qquad\qquad \Gamma(1) = 1 \qquad\qquad \Gamma(n+1) = n!$$

$$\Gamma(\frac{1}{2}) = \sqrt{\pi}$$

The so-called Euler reflection formula also holds:

$$\Gamma(1-z)\Gamma(z) = \frac{\pi}{\sin(\pi z)}$$

The Euler beta function is also called Euler integral and is defined as:

$$\beta(x, y) = \int_0^1 t^{x-1}(1-t)^{y-1}dt$$

121

Both the real parts of x and y are positive. The Euler beta function is symmetric with respect to the exchange of the variables x and y. The following identities hold:

$$\beta(1,1) = 1$$

$$\beta(\frac{1}{2},\frac{1}{2}) = \pi$$

There is a relationship between the beta function and the gamma function given by:

$$\beta(x, y) = \frac{\Gamma(x)\Gamma(y)}{\Gamma(x+y)}$$

A complex series is said to be convergent if the sum of the first n terms converges. Necessary condition for convergence is:

$$\lim_{n\to\infty} z_n = 0$$

If a complex series is absolutely convergent, then it is also convergent. A necessary and sufficient condition for a complex series to converge is given by the following relation:

$$\forall \varepsilon > 0, \exists N > 0 : \forall p \in N^+, n > N \mid \left| \sum_{j=n+1}^{n+p} (a_j + ib_j) \right| < \in$$

For series of complex functions, Weierstrass' first theorem states that, if the terms of a series are analytic functions in a simply connected domain, the series is an analytic function in the same domain. Weierstrass' second theorem states that, if a series of analytic functions in a connected and closed domain is uniformly convergent, then it can be derived term by term n times.

For positive complex power series, Abel's theorem holds, according to which, if the series converges at a point, then it converges uniformly at every point inside a circle of radius equal to the distance between the point of convergence and the center of the series of powers.

XV – Complex analysis

The radius of convergence is established according to the Cauchy-Hadamard formula:

$$R = \lim_{n \to \infty} \left| \frac{a_n}{a_{n+1}} \right|$$

Within this radius, the series converges uniformly and not absolutely. The sum of a positive power series is analytic in its circle of convergence, furthermore every positive power series is a Taylor series of the sum function. In conclusion, the analyticity of a complex function is equivalent to the expandability of the same function into a Taylor series.

To develop a complex power series even with negative terms, Laurent's theorem for expansions in two-sided series is necessary. Given a holomorphic function in a set defined as follows:

$$A = \left\{ z \in C : R_1 < |z - z_0| < R_2 \right\}$$

Therefore, having an isolated singularity, this expansion in bilateral series holds:

$$f(z) = \sum_{n=0}^{+\infty} c_n (z - z_0)^n + \sum_{n=1}^{+\infty} \frac{c_{-n}}{(z - z_0)^n}$$

The values of the coefficients c are numbers, in particular $c_{-1} = \mathrm{Re}\, s(f, z_0)$.

From Laurent's theorem derives the Laurent series which is a complex power series, also including terms of negative degree. The Laurent series can be generalized as follows:

$$f(z) = \sum_{n=-\infty}^{\infty} a_n (z - c)^n$$

$$a_n = \frac{1}{2\pi i} \oint_\gamma \frac{f(z)dz}{(z - c)^{n+1}}$$

XV – Complex analysis

The negative part of Laurent's series is called the main part, the positive part the regular part. If all the negative coefficients of the Laurent series are zero, it coincides with the Taylor series. From Laurent's theorem we see that the region of convergence is not a circle but an annulus.

XVI – FUNCTIONAL ANALYSIS

Functional analysis is that part of mathematical analysis that deals with the study of spaces of functions. In this book, we have already presented several functional analysis results, but now we are going to examine them systematically.

We define embedding as a relationship between two mathematical structures such that one contains a subset of the other and retains its properties. Essentially, immersion extends the concept of set inclusion to functional analysis. A mathematical structure is immersed in another if there is an injective function such that the image of the first structure according to the function preserves all, or even only part, of the mathematical structures.

Set inclusion is an immersion that is called canonical. A topological embedding between two topological spaces is an embedding if it is a homeomorphism. An embedding between metric spaces is a relation which maintains the concept of distance, up to a bias factor.

Given a topological space and two subsets V and W of it, V is said to be compactly embedded in W if the closure of V is compact and if:

$$V \subseteq Cl(V) \subseteq Int(W)$$

Given two normed spaces (we will describe their characteristics shortly) one of which is included in the other, if the inclusion function is continuous then we say that the first is continuously immersed in the second. Furthermore, if any bounded set in the first space is precompact in the other space (that is, any subsequence in that bounded set has a subsequence that is Cauchy in the reference norm), then the first space is compactly embedded in the second.

A particularly important result of mathematical analysis in functional analysis is the Ascoli-Arzelà theorem. A sequence of uniformly bounded continuous functions is equicontinuous if:

$$|f_n(t) - f_n(\tau)| < \varepsilon \qquad |t - \tau| < \delta$$

The theorem states that an equicontinuous and uniformly bounded sequence admits a uniformly convergent subsequence.

XVI – Functional analysis

A pseudometric space is a space that has the same characteristics as a metric space except that the distance is different from zero for each pair of distinct points.

We say ultrametric space, a space in which the triangular inequality takes this form:

$$d(x, z) \leq \max\{d(x, y), d(y, z)\}$$

We define the norm on a real or complex vector space as a homogeneous function, positive definite and such for which the triangular inequality holds:

$$\|x\| \geq 0 \quad \forall x \in X \|\lambda x\| = |\lambda| \|x\|$$
$$\|x + y\| \leq \|x\| + \|y\|$$

The following function of n-dimensional R and C is called p-norm:

$$\|\mathbf{x}\|_p := \left(\sum_{i=1}^{n} |x_i|^p \right)^{\frac{1}{p}}$$

Norm 1 is the simple sum of the absolute values, norm 2 is the so-called Euclidean norm:

$$\|\mathbf{x}\| := \sqrt{\sum_{i=1}^{n} x_i^2}$$

The infinite norm is instead defined as follows:

$$\|\mathbf{x}\|_\infty := \max_i |x_i|$$

Each norm induces a metric through the distance defined as follows:

$$d(x, y) := \|x - y\|$$

For example, the Euclidean norm induces the Euclidean metric in a space, called precisely Euclidean. Two norms are equivalent if there exist two constants such that the following relation holds:

$$c\|x\|_1 \leq \|x\|_2 \leq C\|x\|_1$$

All the norms definable on a vector space of finite dimension are equivalent and induce the same topology, equivalent to the standard Euclidean one.

A norm for which only the properties of homogeneity and triangle inequality hold is called a semi-norm.

The following quantity is called uniform norm of a function, defined on a domain D:

$$\|f\|_\infty = \sup_{x \in D} |f(x)|.$$

If the function is bounded, this value is finite and is also called the norm of the sup. If the function is continuous in a compact set, then the supremum is reached by a maximum and then it is called the norm of the maximum.

If the vector space is defined on a space of matrices, then the norm is called matrix. In particular, the sub-multiplication property also holds for square matrices:

$$\|AB\| \leq \|A\|\|B\|$$

It is easy to define a generic matrix norm p like this:

$$\|A\|_p = \left(\sum_{i=1}^{m} \sum_{j=1}^{n} |a_{ij}|^p \right)^{1/p}$$

A space in which a norm is defined is called normated, one in which a semi-norm is defined is called semi-normed. A complete normed space is called a Banach space.

In Banach spaces the theorems about fixed points are of particular importance. A fixed point is a point which coincides with its image,

XVI – Functional analysis

therefore x=f(x). A topological space is said to have fixed point properties if for every continuous function there is a fixed point.

We define contraction as a function such that there exists a real constant k between 0 and 1 for which:

$$d(f(x), f(y)) \leq k\, d(x, y) \quad \forall x, y \in X$$

Then the contraction theorem (also called Banach's fixed point theorem) states that, given a contraction in a complete non-empty metric space, there is only one fixed point mapped by the contraction.

A contractive function is a continuous function between metric spaces that reduces distances, but in a weaker way than a contraction. Every contraction is therefore a contractive function. The following extension of the contraction theorem holds: a contractive function defined in a compact has only one fixed point.

A non-expansive function is a continuous function between metric spaces that does not spread points apart. This function is Lipschitz with Lipschitz constant equal to one. A non-expansive function defined in a compact and convex set has only one fixed point. Furthermore, the Browder-Gohde-Kirk theorem holds, according to which a non-expansive function of a bounded, closed and convex subset of a Banach space has only one fixed point.

Brouwer's fixed point theorem states that every continuous function defined in a compact, convex, nonempty subset of n-dimensional R has at least one fixed point. In particular, in a Euclidean space, every continuous function mapping the unit ball to itself has at least one fixed point.

An extension of this theorem is given by Schauder's fixed point theorem. Given a closed, convex, nonempty subset of a Banach space, a compact-image continuous function defined in this subset has at least one fixed point.

Schauder's fixed point theorem states that a continuous function in a compact, convex, nonempty set of a Banach space has at least one fixed point. Another variant of this theorem defines the set as convex and closed and the function that sends this set to a non-empty compact subset.

The Leray-Schauder fixed point theorem states that given a continuous and compact function A in a Banach space and defined a set like this:

$$\{u \in X \mid \exists\, \lambda \in [0, 1) : u = \lambda\, A[u]\}$$

If it is bounded then A has a fixed point.

Kellogg's uniqueness theorem builds on Brouwer's theorem and states that, under additional assumptions, the fixed point is unique. These hypotheses are the differentiability of the function, the diversity with respect to 1 of the eigenvalue of the differential and the non-existence of fixed points at the boundary of the subset.

Other fixed point theorems derive from Brouwer's theorem. Rothe's theorem states that a compact function contained in a convex, bounded and open set of a Banach space has a fixed point. Tikhonov's theorem states that a continuous function defined in a compact, convex and non-empty set of a locally convex topological vector space has at least one fixed point. Kakutani's theorem extends Brouwer's theorem to multivalued functions: given a finite-dimensional Euclidean space and a compact, convex, nonempty subset, a multivalued function from this subset to the set of parts that is closed and that is a non-empty convex subset of this subset, has at least one fixed point.

For a Banach space, the Banach-Alaoglu-Bourbaki theorem also holds, according to which in a separable Banach space, every bounded sequence admits a weakly convergent subsequence.

A Hilbert space H is a vector space (real or complex) on which an inner product, called the inner product, is defined such that the distance induced by the product produces a complete metric space. The scalar product is denoted according to the classical brackets (bra and ket) and the norm in a Hilbert space is defined as follows:

$$\|v\| := \sqrt{\langle v, v \rangle}$$

While the induced distance is the following:

$$d(u, v) = \sqrt{\langle u - v, u - v \rangle}$$

Given a set K contained in a Hilbert space, the following subspace is called orthogonal completion of K:

$$K^\perp = \{v \in H \mid \langle u, v \rangle = 0 \ \forall u \in K\}$$

129

XVI – Functional analysis

Two vectors are orthogonal if their dot product is zero. Vectors that are orthogonal and with unit norm are called orthonormal. The Cauchy-Schwarz inequality holds:

$$| \langle v, w \rangle |^2 \leq \langle v, v \rangle \langle w, w \rangle$$

The parallelogram identity:

$$\|v + w\|^2 + \|v - w\|^2 = 2\|v\|^2 + 2\|w\|^2$$

And the extension of the Pythagorean theorem, called Parseval identity:

$$\| \sum_{k=1}^{\infty} v_k \|^2 = \sum_{k=1}^{\infty} \|v_k\|^2$$

Furthermore, Bessel's inequality holds: given a countable set of orthonormal vectors, we have:

$$\langle v, v \rangle = \|v\|^2 \geq \sum_{k=1}^{\infty} |\langle v, e_k \rangle|^2$$

Every Hilbert space has an orthonormal basis which is called the Hilbert basis, which generates a dense subspace in the Hilbert space.
It goes without saying that every Hilbert space is a Banach space. A Banach space is Hilbert space if and only if its norm is induced by an inner product.
A topological space containing a dense and countable subset is said to be separable: finite-dimensional Hilbert spaces are always separable. A Hilbert space is separable if and only if it has an orthonormal basis of countable cardinality.
Examples of finite dimensional Hilbert spaces are the n-dimensional vector space R, endowed with the usual Euclidean scalar product, and the n-dimensional vector space C endowed with the standard Hermitian form:

$$\left\langle \vec{a}, \vec{b} \right\rangle = \sum_{i=1}^{n} a_i^* b_i$$

In a Hilbert space particular polynomials are defined which are orthogonal bases. In particular, the Hermite polynomials are defined as follows:

$$H_n(x) = (-1)^n e^{x^2} \frac{d^n}{dx^n} e^{-x^2}$$

And the Laguerre polynomials:

$$L_n(x) = \frac{e^x}{n!} \frac{d^n}{dx^n} (e^{-x} x^n)$$

In both cases, n is a natural number. There is this relationship between the two polynomial series:

$$H_{2n}(x) = (-1)^n 2^{2n} n! L_n^{(-1/2)}(x^2)$$

A fundamental result of functional analysis is the definition of a new type of measurement with respect to what is usually done by Cauchy-Riemann. We define measure as a function, countably additive, defined on an algebra of subsets of a given set. The structures that are part of algebra are called measurable sets. A space denoted by the algebra and the set is said to be measurable according to the definite measure; a measurable function is an application between two measurable spaces, in particular the identity function is a measurable function on any measurable space.

A k-cell is defined as a set of this type:

$$W = \{(x_1, \ldots, x_k) \in \mathbb{R}^k \mid \quad a_i < x_i < b_i \quad \text{per ogni } i = 1, \ldots, k\}$$

We define the volume of a k-cell as:

$$\text{vol}(W) = \prod_{i=1}^{k} (b_i - a_i)$$

131

The measure that coincides with this volume is called Lebesgue measure and the algebra sets defined therein are called Lebesgue sets or sets measurable according to Lebesgue; this measure is invariant under translation. If a set is the disjoint union of a finite number of disjoint sets Lebesgue measurable then it too is Lebesgue measurable; moreover, for any Lebesgue-measurable set, its complement is also measurable. Unions and intersections of Lebesgue-measurable sets are Lebesgue-measurable and a subset of a Lebesgue-measurable set has a measure less than or equal to that of the starting set.

A Lebesgue set has measure zero if it can be covered with a countable set of products of n intervals whose total volume is at most an infinitesimal. All countable sets have zero Lebesgue measure, as do lines and circles in RxR.

A property is said to be present "almost everywhere" when it holds at all points in a set, except at most in a subset of zero measure. For example, the Dirichlet function is zero almost everywhere.

With this new conception of measurement it is natural to define a new type of integral, called Lebesgue, which generalizes the Riemann integral presented up to now.

We define a simple function as a finite linear combination of indicator functions of measurable sets. The Lebesgue integral of a measurable function on the set F, with respect to the Lebesgue measure, is defined as follows:

$$\int_F f \, d\mu := \sup \int_F s d\mu$$

Where the upper bound is evaluated between all simple functions between 0 and f. The set of functions such that the Lebesgue integral is finite is called the set of Lebesgue integrable functions. The Lebesgue integral of a complex function is obtained by decomposing the integral into four additive pieces (two for the real part, two for the imaginary part, in which one is for the positive part and the other for the negative). The properties of the Riemann integral on linearity,additivity, monotonicity, homogeneity and nullity remain valid; in addition, if the Lebesgue measure of the set F is zero, the Lebesgue integral is always zero.

If two functions are equal almost everywhere, then they have identical Lebesgue integral. For the Lebesgue integral the exchange between the operation of limit and that of integral holds (the so-called passage to the limit under the sign of integral) under appropriate hypotheses, much milder than those relating to the Riemann integral (in fact in this last case uniform convergence is required).

The monotonic convergence theorem states that given a monotonic sequence of non-negative measurable functions for which:

$$\lim_{n \to \infty} f_n(x) \to f(x) \quad \forall x \in E$$

Then f is measurable and we have:

$$\lim_{n \to \infty} \int_E f_n d\mu = \int_E f d\mu$$

The dominated convergence theorem states that if a sequence of measurable functions converges almost everywhere and is dominated by a non-negative function we have:

$$\int_E \lim_{n \to \infty} f_n = \lim_{n \to \infty} \int_E f_n$$

Lebesgue's theorem generalizes the fundamental theorem of integral calculus to Lebesgue integrable functions: the derivative of the integral of an integrable Lebesgue function is almost everywhere equal to the starting function.

On a measurable space, the closure of the subset whose points have all the measures of their neighborhood positive is called the support of the measure. A mollifier is a non-negative function, infinitely derivable with continuity in n-dimensional R, having unit integral in n-dimensional R and with support contained in the ball of radius equal to the inverse of n.

A function is said to have compact support if its support is a compact subset of a topological space; sums and products of functions in compact support are still in compact support. Given a locally integrable function in n-dimensional R and a function with compact support, then the Lebesgue integral given by their product always has finite value.

Functional spaces of particular classes of measurable functions are called Lebesgue spaces. The space of functions with pth integrable power is called space L^p and is a Lebesgue space, where p is a real

number, greater than or equal to one. Lebesgue spaces are Banach spaces, furthermore if p=2 we also have a Hilbert space.
For finite Lebesgue spaces the norm p (which is a complete norm) is defined:

$$\|f\|_p = \left(\int_X |f|^p d\mu\right)^{\frac{1}{p}}$$

Lebesgue L^p space is a complex vector space. If the space has an infinite dimension, the norm is defined as the norm of the inferior, corresponding to the norm of the superior already presented.
In the case of p=1 we speak of spaces of integrable Lebesgue functions, for p=2 we have the integrable square functions. In particular, for p=2 the norm is induced by the following scalar product:

$$\langle f, g \rangle = \int_X \overline{f(x)} g(x) dx$$

A dual space of a space L^p (with finite p and different from one) is called a space L^q such that:

$$\frac{1}{p} + \frac{1}{q} = 1.$$

The dual space is the space of linear and continuous functionals and is isomorphic to the starting space. Every space L^p (with finite p) constructed from an open set of Euclidean space is separable. If p<q then L^q it is a subspace of L^p (obviously if the measure of the set is finite).
In spaces L^p, Holder's inequality holds. Taking a space L^p and its dual we have:

$$\|fg\|_1 \leq \|f\|_p \|g\|_q$$

If p=q=2 this inequality coincides with the Cauchy-Schwarz one.

XVI – Functional analysis

Again in spaces L^p, Minkowski's inequality holds, for functions with positive values:

$$\|f + g\|_p \leq \|f\|_p + \|g\|_p$$

Poincaré's inequality also holds, when p assumes a finite value:

$$\|u\|_{L^p(\Omega)} \leq C\|\nabla u\|_{L^p(\Omega)}$$

It can be seen that the gradient norm is equivalent to the usual norm, in particular in Hilbert spaces a dot product on gradients equivalent to the normal dot product holds:

$$(u, v)_{H_0^1(\Omega)} = \int_\Omega \nabla u \nabla v \, \mathrm{d}^n x$$

In the case of infinite dimensional Lebesgue spaces, if the boundary is Lipschitz, the Poincaré-Wirtinger inequality holds:

$$\|u - u_\Omega\|_{L^p(\Omega)} \leq C\|\nabla u\|_{L^p(\Omega)},$$

Having thus defined the integral mean of u on an open generic of n-dimensional R:

$$u_\Omega = \frac{1}{|\Omega|} \int_\Omega u(y) \, \mathrm{d}y$$

We denote with lowercase l^p the Lebesgue spaces of sequences. In particular, the space l^2 is the space of summable square sequences:

$$\ell^2(\mathbb{R}) = \left\{ \{x_n\}_{n \in \mathbb{N}}, \, x_i \in \mathbb{R} \,\middle|\, \sum_{k=1}^\infty |x_k|^2 < \infty \right\}$$

This space is vector and is also metric with the following distance:

$$d(\vec{x}, \vec{y}) = \left(\sum_{k=1}^{\infty} |x_k - y_k|^2 \right)^{\frac{1}{2}}$$

Such a space has dense countable subsets, is separable, complete, normated with the following norm and endowed with the following scalar product:

$$\|\vec{x}\| = \left(\sum_{k=1}^{\infty} |x_k|^2 \right)^{1/2}$$

$$\langle \{x_n\} | \{y_n\} \rangle = \sum_{k=1}^{\infty} x_k y_k$$

The space is therefore Hilbert and also Euclidean. Typically, a space l^p is Banach with the norm:

$$\|\vec{x}\| = \left(\sum_{k=1}^{\infty} |x_k|^p \right)^{1/p}$$

If the measure of the set on which the sequences are defined is finite, then if p<q every space l^p is contained in the space l^q. Such spaces are a case of Lebesgue spaces of functions where the defining set of the functions is the set of natural numbers.

The relationship between space l^2 and space L^2 is given by the Riesz-Fischer theorem, which states that, in a complete space, every summable square sequence defines an integrable square function; in particular the elements of the sequence are the Fourier coefficients of a vector of L^2. Furthermore, a function is square-integrable if and only if the series of Fourier coefficients converges in space l^2.

The Riesz representation theorem for Hilbert spaces states that, given a Hilbert space with its dual, if x is an element of H, the function thus defined:

$$\phi_x(y) = \langle y, x \rangle \quad \forall y \in H$$

It is an element of dual space. A corollary of this theorem considers the function as a scalar in bilinear form such that:

$$\phi(\mathbf{x}, a\mathbf{y} + b\mathbf{z}) = a\phi(\mathbf{x},\mathbf{y}) + b\phi(\mathbf{x},\mathbf{z})$$
$$\phi(a\mathbf{x} + b\mathbf{y}, \mathbf{z}) = \bar{a}\phi(\mathbf{x},\mathbf{z}) + \bar{b}\phi(\mathbf{y},\mathbf{z})$$
$$|\phi(\mathbf{x},\mathbf{y})| \leq C\|\mathbf{x}\|\|\mathbf{y}\|$$

In this case there is a unique linear application that satisfies this relation:

$$\phi(\mathbf{x},\mathbf{y}) = (A\mathbf{x},\mathbf{y}) \qquad \forall \mathbf{x}, \mathbf{y} \in H$$

This theorem is fundamental for defining the orthogonal projections of generic elements of Hilbert spaces and for the so-called spectral decomposition, which we will discuss shortly.

A function of a real variable satisfies Holder's condition if:

$$|f(x) - f(y)| \leq C|x - y|^{\alpha}$$

Where C is a positive constant, while alpha is between 0 and 1 and is called the Holder exponent. If the function satisfies this condition, it is called Holderian and generalizes Lipschitianity (which occurs only when alpha is zero or one). The space of functions satisfying the Holder condition together with the nth order derivatives is a topological and Euclidean vector space called Holder space which has this semi-norm:

$$\|f\|_{C^{n,\alpha}} = \max_{|\beta|\leq n}\sup_{x\in\Omega}|D^{\beta}f(x)| + \max_{|\beta|=n}\|D^{\beta}f\|_{C^{0,\alpha}}$$

Another result of primary importance of functional analysis is the operative vision, above all for its applications in the field of theoretical physics.

A linear operator between vector spaces is a linear transformation defined on a linear manifold contained in the vector space. A linear operator is continuous at a point if the normal continuity relation holds. In normed spaces, a linear operator is globally continuous if and only if it is continuous at every point, and it is continuous if and only if it is bounded.

XVI – Functional analysis

The norm of a linear and continuous operator between normed spaces is given by:

$$\|A\|_{\mathcal{L}(N,M)} = \sup_{\|x\|_N \leq 1} \|Ax\|_M$$

It can be seen that every linear and continuous operator on Banach spaces is Lipschitz.

It is possible to define different topologies on Banach or Hilbert spaces for continuous linear operators, called operator topologies. The strong ordinary operator topology is thus defined for a sequence of linear and continuous operators:

$$T_n x \to T x \qquad \forall x \in H$$

The ordinary topology is weak like this:

$$F(T_n x) \to F(T x) \qquad \forall F \in H^*$$

While the uniform:

$$\|T_n - T\| \to 0 \qquad \forall x \in H$$

Convergence in uniform topology implies the ordinary strong one which, in turn, implies the weak one.

A bounded linear operator L is a continuous linear operator between normed vector spaces X and Y such that:

$$\sup_{x \neq 0} \left[\frac{\|Lx\|_Y}{\|x\|_X} \right] < \infty \qquad \forall x \in X$$

An operator A is said to be bounded relative to another operator B if it holds

$$D(B) \subset D(A) \qquad \|Au\| \leq a_1 \|u\| + a_2 \|Bu\| \qquad u \in D(B)$$

A linear operator A is closed on a Banach space B, if for every convergent sequence:

$$\lim_{n \to \infty} A x_n = y \in B$$

We have:

$$Ax = y$$

Any closed operator defined over all space is bounded.
Given two Banach spaces and a continuous and bounded linear operator that connects them, the adjunct operator of this operator is another bounded linear operator given by:

$$(T'\phi)(x) = \phi(Tx) \qquad \forall x \in X \quad \forall \phi \in Y^*$$

Where dual spaces have been indicated with an asterisk.
In Hilbert spaces, called A a continuous linear operator such that:

$$L_w(\mathbf{v}) = \langle A\mathbf{v}, \mathbf{w} \rangle$$

If the operator is also bounded, then its adjunct operator is defined as follows:

$$\langle A\mathbf{v}, \mathbf{w} \rangle = \langle \mathbf{v}, A^*\mathbf{w} \rangle$$

In matrix mathematics, the matrix corresponding to the added operator is the complex conjugate transpose of the matrix of the starting operator A. The following property holds:

$$\|A\| = \|A^*\|$$

The addition operator of an addition is equal to the departure operator; if the starting operator is invertible, so is the adjoint. The sum of operators added is equal to the operator added to the sum if at least one of the operators is bounded, while the product has the following property:

$$(AB)^* = B^* A^*$$

In addition, the following properties hold:

$$\ker A^* = (\operatorname{im} \ A)^{\perp} \qquad\qquad (\ker A^*)^{\perp} = \overline{\operatorname{im} \ A}$$

If, on the other hand, the operator is not limited, these results are not valid.

If the added operator coincides with the starting one, then it is said to be self-adjoint.

A unitary operator U is an isomorphism between two Hilbert spaces that preserves the dot product:

$$(\phi, \psi) = (U\phi, U\psi) \qquad \forall \phi, \psi \in \mathcal{H}_1$$

Unitary operators always have unitary norm.

Given two Banach spaces, a bounded linear operator is said to be compact if it maps bounded sets into sets whose closure is compact. The canonical form for compact operators on Hilbert spaces is given by the dot product of two sets of orthonormal vectors:

$$T = \sum_{n=1}^{N} \lambda_n \langle \phi_n, \cdot \rangle \psi_n \qquad 1 \leq N \leq \infty$$

If a sequence of compact operators converges to T, then T is compact. An operator is compact if and only if its adjoint is also compact.

Fredholm's analytic theorem states that a compact operator on a Hilbert space is such that the problem Tf=f has a solution. This will come in handy for solving integral equations.

The Hilbert-Schmidt theorem states that given a compact and self-adjoint operator A defined on a Hilbert space, we have a complete orthonormal basis such that:

$$A\phi_n = \lambda_n \phi_n$$

A normal operator N in a Hilbert space is an endomorphism from H in H for which:

$$N N^* = N^* N.$$

For normal operators it is also true that:

$$\mathrm{Ker}(N^*) = \mathrm{Ker}(N)$$
$$\mathrm{Im}(N^*) = \mathrm{Im}(N)$$

A differential operator is an operator defined as a function of the operation of usual derivation. Linear differential operators combine the properties of derivation with those of matrix mathematics, especially for the properties of sum, product, and commutation. For differential operators, you can define the adjoint operator as before.

Once the types of operators have been defined, the definition of the spectral theorem becomes central.

For a real finite-dimensional vector space of dimension n with inner product, an endomorphism of such a space is self-adjoint if and only if there exists an orthonormal basis of eigenvectors; the endomorphism is, consequently, diagonalizable.

If the finite-dimensional vector space is complex, then we have the same statement, but instead of the dot product we have a positive definite Hermitian form. In this case, the orthonormal basis has real eigenvalues if and only if the endomorphism is self-adjoint, while if it is unitary then the modulus of the eigenvalues of the orthonormal basis is equal to one.

For infinite dimensional spaces, the spectral theorem states that a bounded and self-adjoint operator defined on a Hilbert space is a multiplication operator. A writing of this type is called spectral representation of the operator A (U is a generic unitary operator):

$$(UAU^{-1}\psi)_n(\lambda) = \lambda\psi_n(\lambda)$$
$$\psi = \{\psi_n(\lambda)\} \in \bigoplus_{n=1}^{N} L^2(\mathbb{R}, d\mu_n)$$

For unbounded and self-adjoint operators on infinite dimensional Hilbert spaces, then it is possible to carry out this operation (with U always denoting a generic unitary operator):

$$(UAU^{-1}\phi)(x) = f(x)\phi(x)$$

The operation of diagonalizing an operator with respect to an orthonormal basis is called spectral decomposition.

XVI – Functional analysis

For the finite-dimensional case the spaces on which the operator is defined are orthogonal to each other and in direct sum; therefore the operator can be decomposed into single orthogonal projections on different subspaces. In this case, the spectral decomposition is a special case of the Schur matrix decomposition.

For the infinite-dimensional case if the operator is normal and bounded then the theorem states that there is a unique measure on a projector of the operator such that:

$$A = \int_{\sigma(A)} z \, dP^A(x,y) \qquad z := (x,y) \to x + iy \in \mathbb{C} \quad (x,y) \in \mathbb{R}^2$$

Having defined the operator spectrum as the projector mount:

$$\sigma(A) = \mathrm{supp}(P^A)$$

If the operator is also self-adjoint it is easy to diagonalize it like this:

$$A = \int_{\sigma(A)} \lambda \, dP^A \qquad f(A) = \int_{\sigma(A)} f(\lambda) \, dP^A$$

If the operators are not bounded, it is necessary to introduce the Cayley transform, which we will do in the next chapter.

The spectrum and the resolvent of an operator defined on a Banach space coincide with those of its adjunct. In a Hilbert space, instead, it holds that:

$$\sigma(T^*) = \{\lambda : \bar{\lambda} \in \sigma(T)\} \qquad R_\lambda(T^*) = R_\lambda(T)^*$$

If the operator is self-adjoint in a Hilbert space, then the spectrum has real eigenvalues. Moreover, eigenvalues related to distinct eigenvectors are orthogonal.

The Riesz-Schauder theorem states that a compact operator on a Hilbert space has a spectrum formed by a discrete set with no limit points apart from the null one and every non-zero eigenvalue has finite multiplicity.

Other theorems also hold for Banach spaces, including the principle of uniform boundedness. Given a Banach space X, a normed space Y and a family F of continuous linear operators which sends the Banach space X into the normed one Y, if it holds

$$\sup\left\{\,\|Tx\| : T \in F\,\right\} < \infty,$$

Then we have:

$$\sup\left\{\,\|Tx\| : T \in F\,\right\} < \infty,$$

Where T is the generic linear and continuous operator.

The open function theorem states that given a continuous and surjective linear operator T between the Banach spaces X and Y, this operator is an open function, i.e. if U is open in X also T(U) is open in Y.

A consequence of this theorem is the closed graph theorem. Given two sets X and Y and a function T from X to Y then the graph of T is the subset of the Cartesian product XxY. If X and Y are Banach spaces and T is a linear operator, then T is continuous and bounded if and only if its graph is closed in the Cartesian space with the product topology.

A function on a vector space is said to be sublinear if:

$$f(\gamma x) = \gamma f(x) \quad \forall \gamma \in \mathbb{R}_+ \quad \forall x \in V$$
$$f(x + y) \leq f(x) + f(y) \quad \forall x, y \in V$$

The Hahn-Banach theorem states that if a linear function on a vector subspace is dominated by a sublinear function, then there is a definite linear extension over the whole space. In Banach spaces, this theorem states that, defined a linear and continuous function on a subspace of a normed space, there exists an extension on the whole space which is linear and continuous and which has the same norm as the starting function.

A space is called Baire if the countable union of every family of closed sets with empty interior has empty interior. The set of real numbers is an example of a Baire space, like the Cantor set.

Every complete metric space is a Baire space. Every topologically complete space is Baire space, as is every locally compact Hausdorff space. Such statements are known as Baire's category theorem.

Other functional analysis results will be presented in the next chapters.

XVI – Functional analysis

XVII – TRANSFORM

Transforms have been introduced to solve many mathematical problems, in particular differential equations, which we will discuss later.

A first large family of transforms are the integral transforms which are integral applications of a space of functions on another space of functions. The general form of an integral equation is given by:

$$T(f)(s) = \int_a^b K(s,t)f(t)dt$$

Where K(s,t) is the function that characterizes the various transforms and is called kernel.

We begin by considering the Fourier transform, which is also the most important integral transform. The Fourier transform of a function belonging to the Lebesgue space $L^1(R)$ is:

$$\mathcal{F}\{f\}(t) = \hat{f}(t) := \frac{1}{\sqrt{2\pi}} \int_{\mathbb{R}} f(x)e^{-ixt}\,dx \qquad \forall t \in \mathbb{R}$$

We will see that the transform can also be extended to the Hilbert space $L^2(R)$. Fourier's inversion theorem states that if the function and its transform belong to $L^1(R)$, then it is possible to write the inversion formula as follows:

$$f(x) = \frac{1}{\sqrt{2\pi}} \int_{\mathbb{R}} \hat{f}(t)e^{ixt}\,dt$$

This inverse function of the Fourier transform is called the inverse Fourier transform.

The Fourier transform has linearity properties and the following properties:

145

$$g(t) = f(t - a) \Rightarrow \hat{g}(\omega) = \hat{f}(\omega)e^{-ia\omega}$$
$$g(t) = f(t)e^{iat} \Rightarrow \hat{g}(\omega) = \hat{f}(\omega - a)$$
$$g(t) = f(-t) \Rightarrow \hat{g}(\omega) = \hat{f}(-\omega)$$
$$g(t) = f(-t)^* \Rightarrow \hat{g}(\omega) = \hat{f}(\omega)^*$$
$$g(t) = f(t/\lambda) \Rightarrow \hat{g}(\omega) = \lambda\hat{f}(\lambda\omega) \quad \lambda > 0$$
$$g(t) = -itf(t) \Rightarrow \hat{f}'(\omega) = i\omega\hat{f}(\omega)$$

If a function is real and even, then its Fourier transform is real and even, while if the function is real and odd, then its Fourier transform is imaginary and odd.

Given two functions, one of which has compact support and the other can be integrated according to Lebesgue, then the convolution between the two functions is the following relation:

$$(f * g)(t) := \int_{-\infty}^{\infty} f(\tau)g(t - \tau)d\tau = \int_{-\infty}^{\infty} f(t - \tau)g(\tau)d\tau$$

Instead, it is called circular convolution of a periodic function with period T:

$$(x_T * h)(t) \stackrel{\text{def}}{=} \int_{-\infty}^{\infty} h(\tau) \cdot x_T(t - \tau)\, d\tau = \int_{t_o}^{t_o+T} h_T(\tau) \cdot x_T(t - \tau)d\tau$$

$$h_T(t) \stackrel{\text{def}}{=} \sum_{k=-\infty}^{\infty} h(t - kT) = \sum_{k=-\infty}^{\infty} h(t + kT)$$

While the discrete convolution is:

$$(f * g)[n] \stackrel{\text{def}}{=} \sum_{m=-\infty}^{\infty} f[m]\, g[n - m] = \sum_{m=-\infty}^{\infty} f[n - m]\, g[m]$$

If the functions are Lebesgue integrable, then their convolution is also integrable and holds:

$$\|f * g\|_p \leq \|f\|_1 \|g\|_p$$

Young's inequality proves that the convolution is a continuous bilinear function between spaces L^p. The convolution has commutative, associative, distributive properties and the following differentiation rule holds:

$$\mathcal{D}(f * g) = \mathcal{D}f * g = f * \mathcal{D}g$$

For discrete convolution this rule becomes:

$$\mathcal{D}f(n) = f(n+1) - f(n)$$

The convolution theorem states the Fourier transform of the convolution of two functions is equal to the product of the Fourier transforms of the individual functions:

$$\mathcal{F}(f * g) = \mathcal{F}(f) \cdot \mathcal{F}(g)$$

Thanks to the convolution operation it is possible to demonstrate that, given a Lebesgue-integrable function, the Fourier transform exists and is unique.

We define cross-correlation between two functions (or cross-correlation) as the following relationship:

$$R_{xy}(t) = (x \otimes y)(t) \overset{\text{def}}{=} \int_{-\infty}^{\infty} x^*(\tau)\, y(t+\tau)\, d\tau$$

For discrete functions the following holds:

$$R_{xy}[n] = (x \otimes y)[n] \overset{\text{def}}{=} \sum_{m=-\infty}^{\infty} x^*[m]\, y[n+m]$$

This property holds for cross-correlation:

$$\mathcal{F}\{x \otimes y\} = (\mathcal{F}\{x\})^* \cdot \mathcal{F}\{y\},$$

147

If the functions x and y coincide then we speak of autocorrelation:

$$R_x(t) \overset{\text{def}}{=} \int_{-\infty}^{\infty} x^*(\tau)\, x(t + \tau)\, d\tau$$

$$R_x[n] \overset{\text{def}}{=} \sum_{m=-\infty}^{\infty} x^*[m]\, x[n + m]$$

This function has Hermitian symmetry. In signal theory, the Wiener-Khinchin theorem states that the energy spectral density of a signal is the Fourier transform of the autocorrelation of the signal.

Plancherel's theorem states that it is possible to associate to each square integrable function a function, called Fourier transform, also square integrable such that:

$$\|\hat{f}\|_2 = \|f\|_2$$

Also Parseval's theorem holds, already met in the presentation of Hilbert spaces, but here rewritten using the Fourier transform:

$$\int_{-\infty}^{\infty} |A(t)|^2 dt = \int_{-\infty}^{\infty} |\hat{A}(\omega)|^2 d\omega$$

From this theorem we derive a new formula for the energy of a signal:

$$\int_{-\infty}^{+\infty} \|x(t)\|^2 dt = \int_{-\infty}^{+\infty} \|X(f)\|^2 df = E_x$$

The Riemann-Lebesgue lemma states the Fourier transform of an integrable function vanishes at infinity:

$$\int_{-\infty}^{\infty} f(x) e^{-izx}\, dx \to 0 \text{ per } z \to \pm\infty$$

The Schwartz space is the space of functions decreasing faster than a polynomial:

$$\mathcal{S}(\Omega) = \{f \in C^{\infty}(\Omega) \mid ||f||_{\alpha,\beta} < \infty \, \forall \, \alpha, \beta\},$$

Where the norm is defined as follows (having indicated the multi-index derivatives):

$$||f||_{\alpha,\beta} = \sup_{x \in \mathbf{R}^n} |x^{\alpha} D^{\beta} f(x)|$$

This space is vectorial, complex, closed with respect to addition and multiplication by complex scalars, furthermore it is a complete space. The Fourier transform is a linear isomorphism between Schwartz spaces.
We define a function, called Dirac delta, as follows:

$$\int_{-\infty}^{+\infty} \delta(x)\,\phi(x)\,\mathrm{d}\,x = \phi(0)$$

The Dirac delta is, more properly, a distribution (we will discuss it in the next chapter) associated with a function of the Schwartz space:

$$\delta_a[\phi] = \phi(a)$$

The product for a scalar of a Dirac delta is:

$$\int_{-\infty}^{+\infty} a\delta(t)\,\phi(t)\,\mathrm{d}\,t = a \int_{-\infty}^{+\infty} \delta(t)\,\phi(t)\,\mathrm{d}\,t$$

The one with a function is given by:

$$\alpha(t)\,\delta(t - t_0) = \alpha(t_0)\,\delta(t - t_0)$$

The translation acts as a convolution integral:

$$\int_{-\infty}^{+\infty} f(t)\delta(t - T)\,\mathrm{d}\,t = f(T)$$

It also enjoys the reflection property:

XVII – Transform

$$\delta(at) = \frac{1}{|a|}\delta(t)$$

The following derivation and convolution rules apply:

$$\frac{d}{dx}\delta(-x) = -\frac{d}{dx}\delta(x)$$

$$x\delta'(x) = -\delta(x)$$

$$\delta' * f = \delta * f' = f'$$

The Dirac delta can be expressed according to the Fourier transform as follows:

$$\delta(t) = \frac{1}{2\pi}\int_{-\infty}^{+\infty} e^{ikt}\, dk$$

While the Fourier transform of delta is the unit constant:

$$\hat{\delta}(k) = \int_{-\infty}^{+\infty} e^{-i2\pi xk}\delta(x)\, dx = 1$$

Another integral transform is the Laplace transform defined on non-negative real numbers:

$$\mathcal{L}\{f\}(s) = \int_{0}^{+\infty} e^{-st}f(t)\, dt$$

Where s is a generic complex number. The two-sided Laplace transform is defined as follows:

$$\mathcal{L}_u\{f\}(s) = \int_{-\infty}^{\infty} e^{-st}f(t)\, dt$$

The Laplace transform exists for all real numbers such that Re(s)>a where a is a constant defining the region of convergence of the transform.

The inverse Laplace transform is given by:

$$f(t) = \mathcal{L}^{-1}\{F(s)\} = \frac{1}{2\pi i} \lim_{T \to \infty} \int_{\gamma - iT}^{\gamma + iT} e^{st} F(s) \, ds$$

To define the region of convergence of a locally integrable function, we see that the Laplace transform converges if such a limit exists:

$$\lim_{R \to \infty} \int_0^R f(t) e^{-ts} \, dt$$

While it converges absolutely if there is such an integral according to Lebesgue:

$$\int_0^\infty |f(t) e^{-ts}| \, dt$$

The Laplace transform has the properties of linearity and the following rules of derivation, integration and translation:

$$\mathcal{L}\{f^{(n)}\} = s^n \mathcal{L}\{f\} - s^{n-1} f(0^+) - \cdots - f^{(n-1)}(0^+) = s^n \mathcal{L}\{f\} - \sum_{k=1}^{n} s^{n-k} \frac{d^{k-1} f(0)}{dt^{k-1}}$$

$$\mathcal{L}\{tf(t)\} = -\mathcal{L}\{f\}'(s) \qquad \mathcal{L}\left\{\frac{f(t)}{t}\right\} = \int_s^\infty \mathcal{L}\{f\}(\sigma) \, d\sigma$$

$$\mathcal{L}\left\{\int_0^t f(\tau) \, d\tau\right\} = \frac{1}{s} \mathcal{L}\{f(t)\}$$

$$\mathcal{L}\{e^{at} f(t)\} = \mathcal{L}\{f\}(s-a) \qquad \mathcal{L}^{-1}\{\mathcal{L}\{f\}(s-a)\} = e^{at} f(t)$$

$$\mathcal{L}\{f(t-a)\Theta(t-a)\} = e^{-as} \mathcal{L}\{f\}(s) \qquad \mathcal{L}^{-1}\{e^{-as} \mathcal{L}\{f\}\} = f(t-a)\Theta(t-a)$$

XVII – Transform

Having indicated in the last reports the Heavyside function (also called step) as that function which is 0 for negative numbers and +1 for positive numbers. Also for the Laplace transform the rule holds that the transform of the convolution is equal to the product of the transforms.
There are two theorems called the initial value and the final value, which state that:

$$f(0) = \lim_{t \to 0} f(t) = \lim_{s \to \infty} s \, \mathcal{L}\{f\}(s)$$
$$f(\infty) = \lim_{t \to \infty} f(t) = \lim_{s \to 0} s \, \mathcal{L}\{f\}(s)$$

Some notable Laplace transforms are as follows:

$$\mathcal{L}\{\delta(t)\} = 1$$
$$\mathcal{L}\{\Theta(t)\} = \frac{1}{s}$$
$$\mathcal{L}\{e^{\alpha t}\} = \frac{1}{s - \alpha}$$
$$\mathcal{L}\{\sin(\alpha t)\} = \frac{\alpha}{s^2 + \alpha^2}$$
$$\mathcal{L}\{\cos(\alpha t)\} = \frac{s}{s^2 + \alpha^2}$$
$$\mathcal{L}\{\sinh(\alpha t)\} = \frac{\alpha}{s^2 - \alpha^2}$$
$$\mathcal{L}\{\ln(t)\} = -\frac{\ln(s) + \gamma}{s}$$
$$\mathcal{L}\{\sqrt[\alpha]{t}\} = s^{-\frac{\alpha+1}{\alpha}} \cdot \Gamma\left(1 + \frac{1}{\alpha}\right)$$

The Fourier transform is none other than the two-sided Laplace transform with only an imaginary argument.
The Laplace-Stieltjes transform is given by the homonymous integral in which g is required to be a function with limited variation:

$$\int e^{-sx} \, dg(x) \qquad s \in \mathbb{C}$$

XVII – Transform

The two-sided and one-sided transform are defined as follows:

$$\{\mathcal{L}^*g\}(s) = \int_{-\infty}^{\infty} e^{-sx}\, dg(x)$$

$$\{\mathcal{L}^*g\}(s) = \int_{0-}^{\infty} e^{-sx}\, dg(x)$$

Many properties of the Laplace transform hold, in particular the convolution theorem.

The Hilbert transform makes use of the Cauchy principal value for improper integrals:

$$H(u)(t) = \text{p.v.} \int_{-\infty}^{\infty} u(\tau)h(t-\tau)\, d\tau = \frac{1}{\pi}\, \text{p.v.} \int_{-\infty}^{\infty} \frac{u(\tau)}{t-\tau}\, d\tau,$$

The Mellin transform is defined as follows:

$$\{\mathcal{M}f\}(s) = \varphi(s) = \int_0^{\infty} x^{s-1} f(x)\, dx$$

If the transform is an analytic function in a strip of the complex plane and c is a real number in that strip such that the integral is absolutely convergent, then it is possible to define the inverse Mellin transform as follows:

$$\{\mathcal{M}^{-1}\varphi\}(x) = f(x) = \frac{1}{2\pi i} \int_{c-i\infty}^{c+i\infty} x^{-s}\varphi(s)\, ds$$

The Mellin transform can be related to the two-sided Laplace transform and the Fourier transform:

$$\{\mathcal{M}f\}(s) = \{\mathcal{L}f(e^{-x})\}(s) = \{\mathcal{F}f(e^{-x})\}(-is)$$

The Steinmetz transform is defined on a continuous set:

$$\mathfrak{s}\left\{f\right\}(\omega) = \frac{\omega}{\pi} \int_{-\frac{\pi}{\omega}}^{\frac{\pi}{\omega}} e^{-i\omega t} f(t)\, dt.$$

This transform admits an inverse transform and is linear. The rules of derivation, integration and translation are given by:

$$\mathfrak{s}\left\{f^{(n)}\right\} = i^n \omega^n \mathfrak{s}\left\{f\right\}$$

$$\mathfrak{s}\left\{\int_0^t f(\tau)\, d\tau\right\} = -\frac{i}{\omega}\mathfrak{s}\{f(t)\}$$

$$\mathfrak{s}\left\{e^{at} f(t)\right\} = \mathfrak{s}\left\{f\right\}(\omega - a)$$

$$\mathfrak{s}\left\{f(t-a)u(t-a)\right\} = e^{-a\omega}\mathfrak{s}\left\{f\right\}(s)$$

The convolution, initial value and final value theorems always hold:

$$f(0) = \lim_{t \to 0} f(t) = \lim_{\omega \to \infty} \omega\, \mathfrak{s}\left\{f\right\}(\omega)$$

$$f(\infty) = \lim_{t \to \infty} f(t) = \lim_{\omega \to 0} \omega\, \mathfrak{s}\left\{f\right\}(\omega)$$

The Steinmetz transform is related to the Fourier transform as follows:

$$2\omega \mathcal{F}\{f\}(\omega) = \frac{\omega}{\pi} \int_{-\pi}^{\pi} e^{-i\omega t} f(t)\, dt$$

The Legendre transform is not an integral transform and applies to real convex functions:

$$f^\star(p) = \sup_x \left(px - f(x)\right) \qquad p \in \mathbb{R}$$

The inverse Legendre transform coincides with the transform. The importance of the Legendre transform is given by the fact that, in mechanics, the Legendre transform of the Lagrangian function is the Hamiltonian.

Another category of transforms is given by discrete transforms. The discrete Fourier transform is the following relation:

$$X_k = \sum_{n=0}^{N-1} x_n e^{-\frac{2\pi i}{N} kn} \qquad k = 0, \ldots, N-1$$

Where within the summation there is a sequence of N complex numbers. The discrete inverse Fourier transform is expressed as follows:

$$x_n = \frac{1}{N} \sum_{k=0}^{N-1} X_k e^{\frac{2\pi i}{N} kn} \qquad n = 0, \ldots, N-1$$

In multiple dimensions, just express the summations for each index. The discrete Fourier transform is an invertible linear transformation which has the property of being able to decompose into orthogonal bases. Plancherel's and Parseval's theorems hold in the form:

$$\sum_{n=0}^{N-1} x_n y_n^* = \frac{1}{N} \sum_{k=0}^{N-1} X_k Y_k^*$$

$$\sum_{n=0}^{N-1} |x_n|^2 = \frac{1}{N} \sum_{k=0}^{N-1} |X_k|^2$$

The transfer can be defined as follows:

$$\mathcal{F}(\{x_n \cdot e^{\frac{2\pi i}{N} nm}\})_k = X_{k-m} \qquad \mathcal{F}(\{x_{n-m}\})_k = X_k \cdot e^{-\frac{2\pi i}{N} km}$$

While the convolution is the circular one and the cross-correlation is given by:

$$\mathcal{F}^{-1}\{\mathbf{X}^* \cdot \mathbf{Y}\}_n = \sum_{l=0}^{N-1} x_l^* \cdot (y_N)_{n+l} \overset{\text{def}}{=} (\mathbf{x} \star \mathbf{y_N})_n$$

It is possible to define from the discrete Fourier transform a discrete-time Fourier transform, obtained by discretizing time according to the Fourier periodicity rule. In this way, it is possible to define remarkable Fourier transforms in discrete time which are widely used in signal theory. Similar properties apply to those found for the discrete and continuous Fourier transform, such as linearity, time and frequency translation, derivation, integration and so on.

The zeta transform generalizes the discrete Fourier transform and is defined, in bilateral form, by:

$$X(z) = \mathcal{Z}\{x[n]\} = \sum_{n=-\infty}^{\infty} x[n]z^{-n}$$

With n integer and z complex number. The one-sided transformation, defined for natural n:

$$X(z) = \mathcal{Z}\{x[n]\} = \sum_{n=0}^{\infty} x[n]z^{-n}$$

The convergence region of the zeta transform is the part of the complex plane where the series converges; in particular it converges for values of z having modulus greater than the radius of convergence thus defined:

$$R = \limsup_{n \to \infty} |f(n)|^{\frac{1}{n}}$$

The inverse zeta transform is defined on a closed counterclockwise path which is located in the convergence region and surrounds the origin of the complex plane:

$$x[n] = \mathcal{Z}^{-1}\{X(z)\} = \frac{1}{2\pi j} \oint_C X(z)z^{n-1}dz$$

If the closed path is given by the unit circle, the inverse zeta transform coincides with the discrete inverse Fourier transform. Similar properties

to those already presented apply, including linearity, temporal translation, temporal inversion, differentiation, convolution, Parseval's theorem, the theorems of the initial value and the final value.
The zeta transform of the Dirac delta is the unit constant, the zeta transform of the discrete Heavyside step function is given by:

$$\frac{1}{1-z^{-1}}$$

The one-sided zeta transform is the Laplace transform of an ideally sampled signal with the following substitution:

$$z \stackrel{\text{def}}{=} e^{sT}$$

The discrete cosine transform in one dimension is defined as follows:

$$C(u) = \alpha(u) \sum_{x=0}^{N-1} f(x)\cos\left[\frac{\pi(2x+1)u}{2N}\right]$$

The orthogonal matrix is defined as matrix Cayley transform:

$$Q = (I - A)(I + A)^{-1}$$

The complex Cayley transform is a conformal map from the complex plane:

$$W: z \mapsto \frac{z - \mathbf{i}}{z + \mathbf{i}}$$

The Cayley transform for linear operators on Hilbert spaces is given by:

$$U = (A - \mathbf{i}I)(A + \mathbf{i}I)^{-1}$$
$$A = \mathbf{i}(I + U)(I - U)^{-1}$$

XVII – Transform

158

XVIII – DISTRIBUTIONS

We call a function of a real-valued real variable that is smooth, compactly supported, and defined on a Euclidean space, the test function. The space of test functions is a vector space denoted by D(U). In this space, a topology is defined as the limit of a succession of elements; the sequence converges if there exists a compact containing the support of all the sequences and if the sequence of the multi-index partial derivatives converges uniformly to the multi-index partial derivative. D(U) is therefore a locally convex and complete topological vector space, satisfying the Heine-Borel condition. A particular test function is the cut-off function which is worth 1 inone set and 0 elsewhere.

We define distribution on U as a continuous linear functional for every convergent sequence belonging to D(U). The vector space of distributions is the dual space of D(U) and is denoted by $D'(U)$. This vector space is locally convex and has a weak topology. In the space of distributions, a sequence converges to the distribution if and only if it converges uniformly in every bounded subset of the space of test functions.

The notation that denotes the dual coupling of a distribution to the test function is the one that uses brackets:

$$(S,\phi) \in D'(U) \times D(U), \langle S,\phi \rangle \in R : (S,\phi) \mapsto \langle S,\phi \rangle$$

To each locally integrable function according to Lebesgue we can associate a distribution, i.e. a linear and continuous functional on D(U), whose value on the test function is given by the Lebesgue integral itself:

$$\langle T_f,\phi \rangle = \int_U f\phi dx$$

Given two locally integrable functions, the distributions associated with them coincide if and only if the two functions are equal almost everywhere. Being locally embeddable, test functions can also be interpreted as distributions. An added operator is defined as an operator such that:

XVIII – Distributions

$$\langle T\varphi,\psi\rangle = \langle \varphi,T^*\psi\rangle$$

If such an operator exists and is continuous, then it can be extended to distributions like this:

$$Tf(\psi) = f(T^*\psi)$$

The complex conjugate of a distribution is calculated as follows:

$$\langle T^*,\phi\rangle = \left(\langle T,\phi^*\rangle\right)^*$$

We define two other distributions, called respectively the real part and the imaginary part:

$$\mathrm{Re}\,T = \frac{1}{2}(T+T^*)$$

$$\mathrm{Im}\,T = \frac{1}{2i}(T-T^*)$$

A distribution is real if T=Re(T). The partial derivative of a test function with respect to a variable is given by:

$$T\varphi = \frac{\partial \varphi}{\partial x_k} \Rightarrow \langle T\varphi,\psi\rangle = \left\langle \frac{\partial \varphi}{\partial x_k},\psi\right\rangle = -\left\langle \varphi,\frac{\partial \psi}{\partial x_k}\right\rangle$$

Therefore, every distribution is infinitely differentiable. The concept of derivative of a distribution can also be extended to distributions of several variables, using the same mechanisms mentioned for ordinary functions. The multiplication of a distribution by a smooth function, i.e. infinitely differentiable, is defined as follows:

$$mT(\psi) = \langle mT,\psi\rangle = \langle T,m\psi\rangle = T(m\psi)$$

A tempered distribution is a distribution which is element of the dual space of the Schwartz space. A tempered distribution is the result of deriving a bounded function from a polynomial. Such distributions form a complete vector topological space with metric defined by the following semi-norms:

$$P_{a,b}(\varphi) = \sup_{x \in R^n} \left| x^a D^b \varphi(x) \right|$$

The function is Schwartz if the semi-norm is not infinite; this family of semi-norms defines a locally convex topology. Since the Schwartz functions are smooth functions, the family of semi-norms is a norm on the Schwartz space.

The Fourier transform transforms the derivation into a multiplication: this means that the Fourier transform of a Schwartz function is also a Schwartz function.

It should be emphasized that every tempered distribution admits a Fourier transform, which instead is not obvious for any distribution. The derivative of a tempered distribution is also a tempered distribution; moreover, all distributions with compact support and all integrable square functions are tempered distributions. A necessary and sufficient condition for a distribution to be tempered is that:

$$\lim_{m \to \infty} T(\varphi_m) = 0 \Leftrightarrow \lim_{m \to \infty} P_{a,b}(\varphi_m) = 0$$

The Fourier transform of a tempered distribution is an automorphism on the Schwartz space and is still a tempered distribution:

$$\langle FT, \phi \rangle = \langle T, F\phi \rangle$$

The relationship between the Fourier transform of a tempered distribution and the derivative operation is:

$$F \frac{dT}{dx} = ixFT$$

Defined as a tempered distribution and a slowly increasing infinitely differentiable function according to Schwartz, their product is again a distribution and the Fourier transform of this product is the convolution between the Fourier transforms of the tempered distribution and that of the function:

$$F(T\psi) = FT * F\psi$$

The convolution of a smooth and compactly supported function with a distribution is given by:

$$\langle f(x) * T, \varphi \rangle = \langle T, f(-x) * \varphi \rangle$$

The convolution of two distributions has the associative property:

$$S * (T * \varphi) = (S * T) * \varphi$$

The convolution of distributions relates to the derivative operation:

$$\partial^a (S * T) = (\partial^a S) * T = S * (\partial^a T)$$

The Dirac delta can be interpreted in the sense of distributions on a suitable space of test functions which is the Schwartz space. The Dirac delta is thus defined as a distribution:

$$\delta_a[\phi] = \phi(a)$$

The first distributional derivative of the delta is as follows:

$$\delta'[\phi] = -\delta[\phi'] = -\phi'(0) \iff \int_{-\infty}^{\infty} \delta'(x)\phi(x)dx = -\int_{-\infty}^{\infty} \delta(x)\phi'(x)dx$$

The nth derivative is therefore:

$$\delta^{(n)}[\phi] = (-1)^n \phi^{(n)}(0)$$

The convolution of the first derivative of the Dirac delta with a smooth and compactly supported function is given by:

$$(\delta' * f)(a) = \delta * f'(a) = f'(a)$$

The most suitable functional and topological setting for distributions are Sobolev spaces; such spaces are vectorial and are equipped with a norm. For the one-dimensional case (therefore for the unit circle), a Sobolev space is a subset of a space L^p formed by the functions whose derivatives, in the sense of distributions, have a norm L^p up to a certain order k. The Sobolev space is therefore characterized by the parameters kep and is defined as follows:

$$W^{k,p} = \left\{ f \in L^p \mid \partial^a f \in L^p, \forall a \leq k \right\}$$

The norm in a Sobolev space is defined as follows:

$$\|f\|_{k,p} = \left(\sum_{i=0}^{k} \left\| f^{(i)} \right\|_p^p \right)^{\frac{1}{p}}$$

Sobolev spaces are therefore Banach spaces.
All Sobolev spaces having p=2 are also Hilbert spaces, therefore they admit an inner product, and are denoted by the letter H. These spaces can be defined starting from the Fourier series and the norm contains the Fourier transform, as a consequence of Parseval's identity. If k=0 we have that the space $H^0 \equiv L^2$. If instead k is not integer, the norm is defined as follows:

$$\|f\|_{2,k}^2 = \sum (1+n^2)^k \left| \hat{f}(n) \right|^2$$

If k is greater than ½ , then, having said A is an open set with a sufficiently regular contour B, one can define a trace P of the function f which is the evaluation of f on the contour B. The regularity of the contour is that it is uniformly belonging to the class C^m, with m greater than or equal to k. The continuous extension to the Sobolev space of H^k the trace causes the functions to lose half the derivative.
Multidimensional Sobolev spaces defined on an open subset of n-dimensional R are those spaces formed by the functions defined on the open set such that the multi-index mixed partial derivative is integrable locally and in the L^p reference space. For these spaces, the definition of norm is not univocal, but norms can be chosen which make these spaces Banach. Furthermore, if p is finite, the spaces are separable.

XVIII – Distributions

The space of test functions is dense in Sobolev space $W^{1,p}$ if p is not infinite.

Interpolation spaces intermediate between Sobolev spaces are particular Besov spaces. A Besov space is the space of functions L^p defined on an open set such that the following semi-norm is finite:

$$|f|_{B_q^s(L^p)} = \begin{cases} \left(\int_0^\infty \left[t^{-s} g_p^m(f,t) \right]^q \frac{dt}{t} \right)^{\frac{1}{q}} \Leftrightarrow 0 < q < \infty \\ \sup_{t \in (0,\infty)} t^{-s} g_p^m(f,t) \Leftrightarrow q = \infty \end{cases}$$

Where s>0, p>0, q>0 and m=[s]+ 1. Insuch spaces the norm is given by:

$$\|f\|_{B_q^s(L^p)} = \|f\|_{L^p} + |f|_{B_q^s(L^p)}$$

In Sobolev spaces a number of remarkable inequalities hold.

Given a continuous and differentiable function with compact support, the Gagliardo-Niremberg-Sobolev inequality holds:

$$\forall 1 \le p < n, \exists C_n(p) : p^* = \frac{pn}{n-p} > p \Rightarrow \|f\|_{L^{p*}} \le C_n(p) \|Df\|_{L^p}$$

Furthermore, Nash's inequality also holds:

$$\forall f \in L^1(R^n) \cap H^1(R^n), \exists C > 0 : \|f\|_{L^2(R^n)}^{1+\frac{2}{n}} \le C \|f\|_{L^1(R^n)}^{\frac{2}{n}} \|Df\|_{L^2(R^n)}$$

Given a function belonging to a Sobolev space defined on a bounded and open subset of n-dimensional R with a class boundary C^1, then we have the Sobolev inequalities:

$$k < \frac{n}{p} \Rightarrow \frac{1}{q} = \frac{1}{p} - \frac{k}{n}, f \in L^q, \|f\|_{L^q} \le C \|f\|_{W^{k,p}}$$

164

$$k > \frac{n}{p} \Rightarrow \gamma = \left[\frac{n}{p}\right] + 1 - \frac{n}{p}, f \in C^{k-\left[\frac{n}{p}\right]-1,\gamma}, \|f\|_{C^{k-\left[\frac{n}{p}\right]-1,\gamma}} \leq C\|f\|_{W^{k,p}}$$

Finally, the Polya-Szego inequality holds:

$$1 \leq p < \infty, f \in W^{1,p}(R^n) \Rightarrow \int_{R^n} \left|\nabla f^*\right|^p dH^n \leq \int_{R^n} \left|\nabla f\right|^p dH^n$$

where H^n is the n-dimensional Hausdorff measure. If p>1 and the Hausdorff measure is such that the gradient is zero, then the equality between the integrals holds and the function f^* is equal almost everywhere to a shift of f. This result is known as the Brothers-Ziemer theorem. We will give a complete definition of the Hausdorff measure talking about fractal geometry.

XVIII – Distributions

XIX – ORDINARY DIFFERENTIAL EQUATIONS

A differential equation is a relationship between a function and some of its derivatives. An equation defined in an interval of the set of real numbers in which the total derivatives of the function with respect to the unknown are present is called ordinary. The order of the highest derivative in the equation is called the order of the equation. One can generalize the defining set of an ordinary differential equation into an open and connected generic contained in the complex space of dimension greater than two.

A solution or integral of the ordinary differential equation is a function that satisfies the equation's relation. An equation is said to be autonomous if the relation does not explicitly depend on the variable and is said to be written in normal form if it can be made explicit with respect to the derivative of maximum degree. The equation is called linear if the solution is a linear combination of the derivatives according to this formula:

$$u^{(n)} = \sum_{i=0}^{n-1} a_i(x)u^{(i)} + r(x)$$

The term r(x) is called source and, if it is zero, the linear differential equation is called homogeneous.

In general, an ordinary differential equation of degree n has n linearly independent solutions, and any linear combination of them is itself a solution.

Given a general solution of the homogeneous equation associated with an ordinary differential equation it is possible to find a particular solution of the equation. This will be clarified shortly by the analytical methods of solving differential equations.

An ordinary differential equation of order n expressed in normal form can be reduced to a system of ordinary differential equations of order one in normal form, through the so-called first order reduction procedure.

The ordinary differential equation of order n can be expressed as follows:

XIX – Ordinary differential equations

$$u^{(n)}(x) = G\left(x, u, u', \ldots, u^{(n-1)}\right)$$

We can define coefficients such that:

$$u'_n = u^{(n)}(x)$$

Then we obtain the following equivalent system for solving the starting equation:

$$\vec{u}' = \vec{f}(x,\vec{u}) = \begin{bmatrix} u_2 \\ \ldots \\ u_n \\ G(x,\vec{u}) \end{bmatrix}$$

To study systems of ordinary equations of order n it is necessary to define the Wronskian ie the determinant of the square matrix constructed by placing the functions in the first row, the first derivative of each function in the second row and so on. If the Wronskian is nonzero at any point in a given interval, then the associated functions are linearly independent and so are the solutions of the differential equation.

Boundary conditions of a differential equation are defined as those conditions that the solution of the differential equation must satisfy on the boundary of the definition set. The necessity of the boundary conditions is due to the fact that a differential equation can admit infinite solutions and only the boundary conditions allow to identify a particular solution which can be unique under suitable hypotheses. There are different types of boundary conditions, but the most common are those of Dirichlet or those of Neumann.

A Dirichlet boundary condition, or of the first kind, places fixed boundary values for the value of the function. A Neumann boundary condition, or of the second kind, places fixed boundary values for the value of the first derivative of the function.

Mixed or Robin boundary conditions are also defined, which fix values for the function in a given part of the boundary and for the first derivative of the function in the complementary part of the boundary.

Initial value problems can be defined, i.e. an ordinary differential equation with a fixed value of the function at a point in the domain: this value is called the initial condition. An initial value problem can be summarized as follows:

$$y'(t) = f(t, y(t))$$
$$y(t_0) = y_0$$

A Cauchy problem is given by the solution of a differential equation of order n which satisfies n-1 different initial conditions. The theorem of existence and uniqueness of a Cauchy problem states that the solution of this problem exists and is unique, provided that the function respects certain hypotheses. In particular, the function must be at least continuous in the neighborhood of each point relating to the initial conditions, be Lipschitz with respect to the variable y and uniform with respect to that x. Under these assumptions, the Cauchy problem is equivalent to the Volterra integral equation, which we will discuss in the next chapters. This theorem guarantees local but not global solutions. To guarantee global solutions, for every initial condition there must exist a single maximum in the open interval of its neighborhood such that every solution satisfying the initial condition is a restriction of the global solution. More generally, the Cauchy-Kovalevskaya theorem demonstrates that if the unknown and the initial conditions of a Cauchy problem are locally analytic functions then an analytic solution exists and is unique.

Analytically calculable solutions of differential equations are called exact. In many cases it is not possible to obtain exact solutions, but it is necessary to resort to numerical methods of resolution; these methods will be presented in the chapter on numerical analysis.

A first-order linear differential equation takes the following canonical form:

$$y' = f(x, y)$$

If f depends only on x, the general solution is found using the fundamental theorem of integral calculus and is as follows:

$$y = \int f(x)\,dx = F(x) + c$$

Where F(x) is a primitive of f(x). Cauchy's problem has this solution:

XIX – Ordinary differential equations

$$y = \int_{x_0}^{x} f(t)dt + y_0$$

If the first order linear differential equation is homogeneous and with constant coefficients of the type:

$$y' + ay = 0$$

The solution is:

$$y = y_0 \cdot e^{-a \cdot (x - x_0)}$$

If the equation is non-homogeneous and with variable coefficients:

$$y' + a(x) \cdot y = f(x)$$

The solution is as follows, where A(x) is a primitive of a(x):

$$y(x) = y_0 \cdot e^{(A(x_0) - A(x))} + e^{-A(x)} \int_{x_0}^{x} f(t)e^{A(t)}dt$$

A second order linear ordinary differential equation has the following expression:

$$y'' + a(x) \cdot y' + b(x) \cdot y = f(x)$$

In the particular case of homogeneous equation with constant coefficients:

$$y'' + a \cdot y' + b \cdot y = 0$$

The solution is given by:

$$y = e^{\alpha x}(c_1 \cos \beta x + c_2 \sin \beta x)$$

The complete equation associated with this homogeneous equation has a solution that greatly depends on the behavior of f(x). Easy resolutions

XIX – Ordinary differential equations

are obtained if f(x) is a polynomial or a multiplication between a polynomial and an exponential function or a trigonometric function (sine or cosine) or a multiplication between a polynomial and a previously mentioned trigonometric function or if it is a linear combination of the expressions just presented. From this particular homogeneous equation derive the so-called harmonic functions, i.e. those functions which satisfy this equation, as it represents, in a fairly general way, any harmonic motion.

If the second order linear differential equation has variable coefficients, as in the more general case, the solutions are found with the method of variations of the constants which will be discussed shortly.

For a linear differential equation of any order, the Wronskian of the solutions of the differential equation is the general solution of the associated homogeneous equation. For the complete equation, we proceed as in the second order using the method of variations of constants.

An exact differential equation is an ordinary differential equation that can be reduced to an exact differential. Given a simply connected and open set and two continuous functions I and J in this set, the implied differential equation is defined by:

$$I(x, y)\, dx + J(x, y)\, dy = 0$$

It is exact if there exists a continuously differentiable function F, called potential, such that:

$$\frac{\partial F}{\partial x}(x, y) = I \qquad \frac{\partial F}{\partial y}(x, y) = J$$

From Schwartz's theorem, a necessary and sufficient condition for the existence of the potential is:

$$\frac{\partial I}{\partial y}(x, y) = \frac{\partial J}{\partial x}(x, y)$$

The general solution is given by:

$$K(x, y) = \int I(x, y)dx + \int \left\{ J(x, y) - \left[\int I(x, y)dx \right]_y \right\} dy + C$$

If the Schwartz equality on mixed derivatives does not hold, but it is possible to find a function, called integration factor, for which the relation holds, then it is possible to reduce the differential equation to an exact one, simply by redefining the implicit functions which appear in the general form of the equation.

A particular type of differential equations are those with separable variables, i.e. of the form:

$$y' = a(x)b(y)$$

The solutions are found by integrating by substitution and separating the variables. This procedure is also an analytical method for the resolution of differential equations which we will also find for those with partial derivatives. The limit of this method is given by the fact that the solutions are, precisely, with separate variables, i.e. it is not possible to find mixed or implicit terms.

Nonlinear differential equations, on the other hand, are difficult to solve analytically as there are no general solutions. A nonlinear separate-variable equation can be solved by the separation-of-variables method.

In the same way, a differential equation of a generic order cannot always be solved in analytical terms, unless it can be reduced, through the Wronskian and Cramer's rule, to simpler cases such as those already explained.

The method of variations of constants allows you to determine the general integral of a linear differential equation of any order. This method consists in substituting the variable in the original differential equation, recalling the Leibnitz rule for the product of the derivatives. For example, for second order linear equations it is possible to make this substitution with respect to the two original solutions:

$$\tilde{y} = c_1(t)y_1(t) + c_2(t)y_2(t)$$

The determinant of the matrix thus obtained is precisely the Wronskian and is non-zero if the solutions are independent.

A particular equation involving differential operators and functional analysis in relation to spectral theory is the Sturm-Liouville equation which is a second order linear differential equation, expressed as follows:

XIX – Ordinary differential equations

$$-\frac{\mathrm{d}}{\mathrm{d}x}\left[p(x)\frac{\mathrm{d}y}{\mathrm{d}x}\right]+q(x)y=\lambda r(x)y \qquad \lambda \in \mathbb{C}$$

Where the functions p(x) and r(x) are positive, while q(x) is real. This equation can be written in the form:

$$Ly = \lambda y$$

Where L is a self-adjoint differential operator that defines a linear transformation. The solution of the Sturm-Liouville equation is equivalent to the solution of the eigenvalue problem of this operator. A particular Sturm-Liouville equation is the Legendre equation:

$$(1-x^2)^2 y'' - 2x(1-x^2)y' + ((l^2+l)(1-x^2)-\alpha^2)y = 0$$

The general solutions are called spherical harmonics, which can be expressed as linearly independent partial solutions of the spherical functions.

$$y(x) = C_1 y_1(x) + C_2 y_2(x)$$

The general solutions are the so-called Legendre polynomials:

$$P_n(x) = (2^n n!)^{-1}\frac{d^n}{dx^n}\left[(x^2-1)^n\right]$$

The Bessel equation is a linear and homogeneous second-order ordinary differential equation:

$$x^2 y'' + xy' + (x^2 - \alpha^2)y = 0$$

The general solutions are called cylindrical harmonics, which can be expressed as linearly independent partial solutions of the cylindrical functions.
Cylindrical functions are Bessel functions of the first kind:

XIX – Ordinary differential equations

$$J_\alpha(x) = (\frac{x}{2})^\alpha \sum_{n=0}^{\infty} \frac{(-1)^n(\frac{x}{2})^{2n}}{n!\Gamma(\alpha+n+1)}$$

Neumann functions (or Bessel functions of the second kind):

$$Y_\alpha(x) = \frac{J_\alpha(x)\cos(\alpha\pi) - J_{-\alpha}(x)}{\sin(\alpha\pi)},$$

And the Hankel functions (or Bessel functions of the third kind):

$$H_\alpha^{(1)}(x) = J_\alpha(x) + iY_\alpha(x)$$
$$H_\alpha^{(2)}(x) = J_\alpha(x) - iY_\alpha(x)$$

Many differential equations can also be solved through the use of transforms, especially the Laplace one.
Some ordinary differential equations play a fundamental role in mathematics as they are models for real physics problems.
A special case of a first order ordinary differential equation is the Bernoulli equation:

$$y' + f(x)y = g(x)y^n$$

With real n. Making this substitution:

$$w = \frac{1}{y^{n-1}}$$

And remembering that:

$$w' = w(n-1)f(x) + (1-n)g(x) = F(x)w + G(x)$$

The general solution is given by:

$$w = e^{\int F}\left(\int Ge^{-\int F} + c\right)$$

XIX – Ordinary differential equations

The d'Alembert equation is a first order differential equation of the type:

$$y = xf(y') + g(y')$$

And it always resolves by substitution.
The Lagrange equation is instead given by:

$$y = x \cdot \psi_1(y') + \psi_2(y')$$

The solution of which is (having redefined the parameters and the unknowns):

$$y = \phi_3(p) \cdot k + \phi_4(p)$$

A special case of this equation is the Clairaut equation:

$$y = xy' + f(y')$$

Whose general solution is:

$$y = Cx + f(C),$$

The Abel differential equation of the first kind, also called the Abel identity, is as follows:

$$\frac{d^2y}{dx^2} + P(x)\frac{dy}{dx} + Q(x)y = 0.$$

And it is equivalent to a script using Wronskian:

$$W(x) = W(0)\exp\left(-\int_0^x P(\xi)\,d\xi\right)$$

The Abel differential equation of the second kind is given by:

$$yy' = f(x)y^2 + g(x)y + h(x)$$

XIX – Ordinary differential equations

And it is solved with the following substitution:

$$y = e^{\int f(x)\,dx} z = Ez$$

A first order autonomous system is a system characterized by a first order autonomous equation of the type:

$$y'(t) = f(y(t))$$

Where f is a continuous function with continuous first derivative. In this equation, the points for which the function vanishes are called equilibrium points since the solution is given by the constant value at that point. If the function f is monotone, then y will also be monotone.

A second-order autonomous system can be reduced to a first-order one by defining an additional variable equal to the first derivative of the function.

A Cauchy problem of an autonomous system of two variables has periodic solutions if the Bendixson-Dulac theorem does not hold. This theorem states that if there is a function for which the following sum:

$$\frac{\partial(\varphi f)}{\partial x} + \frac{\partial(\varphi g)}{\partial y}$$

has the same sign and is non-zero almost everywhere in a simply connected set, then the autonomous system thus defined has no periodic solutions.

$$\frac{dx}{dt} = f(x,y)$$
$$\frac{dy}{dt} = g(x,y)$$

XX – Partial differential equations

XX – PARTIAL DIFFERENTIAL EQUATIONS

A partial differential equation is a differential equation where the partial derivatives of a function of several variables appear:

$$F(D^k u(x), D^{k-1}u(x), \cdots, Du(x), u(x), x) = 0$$

Where k is an integer called order of the equation and is the maximum degree of the derivative present in the equation. A partial differential equation is said to be linear if:

$$\sum_{|\alpha|=k} a_\alpha(x) D^\alpha u = f(x)$$

If f(x)=0 then the equation is called homogeneous. If the equation is in this form, it is said to be semi-linear:

$$\sum_{|\alpha|=k} a_\alpha(x) D^\alpha u + a_0(D^{k-1}u, \cdots, Du, u, x) = 0$$

While it is called quasi-linear if it can be expressed as follows:

$$\sum_{|\alpha|=k} a_\alpha(D^{k-1}u, \cdots, Du, u, x) D^\alpha u + a_0(D^{k-1}u, \cdots, Du, u, x) = 0$$

It goes without saying that it is possible to construct systems of partial differential equations.

A problem related to these equations is said to be well posed if the solution exists, is unique and depends continuously on the data provided. Let's say right away that, even more than ordinary differential equations, partial differential equations depend on the initial conditions and boundary conditions and that, at the same time, the analytical solutions of these equations are difficult to extrapolate and not of absolute validity. In this context, all those numerical resolution methods that will be presented in the chapter on numerical analysis assume a primary role.

For equations in two variables, the first order equation is given by:

177

XX – Partial differential equations

$$F(x, y, u, p, q) = 0$$

$$p = u_x$$

$$q = u_y$$

Having used this notation to indicate the partial derivative operation:

$$u_x = \frac{\partial u}{\partial x}$$

A general solution is given by the complete integral:

$$u_w = \phi(x, y, u, A, w(A))$$

If it is not possible to derive this integral, a system of ordinary differential equations is solved using the method of characteristics. This method constitutes, together with the method of separation of the variables, one of the few analytical methods for solving partial differential equations.

The method makes it possible to find curves, called characteristics, along which the partial differential equation is similar to an ordinary differential equation.

Given a first order quasi-linear partial differential equation:

$$a(x, y)\frac{\partial z}{\partial x} + b(x, y)\frac{\partial z}{\partial y} + c(x, y)z = 0$$

The characteristic curve equations are given by:

$$\frac{dx}{a(x, y, z)} = \frac{dy}{b(x, y, z)} = \frac{dz}{c(x, y, z)}$$

A partial differential equation in two variables of the second order is given by:

$$A(x, y)u_{xx} + 2B(x, y)u_{xy} + C(x, y)u_{yy} + \cdots = 0$$

XX – Partial differential equations

By Schwarz's theorem, mixed second derivatives are equal.
It is possible to distinguish the partial differential equations of the second order into three types as this quantity, called delta, varies:

$$B^2 - AC$$

If this quantity is negative, the equation is called elliptic, if it is zero it is called parabolic, if it is positive it is called hyperbolic.
If the variables are n, instead of two, the equation is elliptic if the eigenvalues are all positive or all negative, it is parabolic if they are all positive or all negative, except one which is zero, it is hyperbolic if there is only one negative eigenvalue (positive), while all others are positive (negative).
We point out that, for hyperbolic equations, the method of characteristics is valid.
An existence and uniqueness result for partial differential equations having analytic coefficients and associated Cauchy problems is given by the Cauchy-Kovalevskaya theorem. The limit of this theorem is given by the fact that existence is local and does not ensure a global solution over the whole domain of definition.
One point that distinguishes partial differential equations from ordinary ones is the weak formulation of the problem. With this diction we intend to find solutions to a problem, called weak, which are understood as distributions and not as classical functions. Therefore the spaces of solutions of partial differential equations are, generally, the Sobolev and Hilbert spaces.
Given a Hilbert space with norm and scalar product and a bilinear form b(u,v) in it such that, if F is a generic functional, we have:

$$b(u, v) = < F, v > \qquad \forall v \in V,$$

if this form is continuous and coercive, i.e. if:

$$|b(u, v)| \leq C\|u\|\|v\| \qquad \forall u, v \in V$$

$$b(v, v) \geq \alpha\|v\|^2 \qquad \forall v \in V$$

the Lax-Milgram lemma states that there is only one solution to the problem. Note how this problem is, in all respects, comparable to a partial differential equation. In essence, this lemma is a condition of existence and uniqueness of weak-form solutions. In numerical analysis the following stability estimate of the solution of the weak problem will also be useful:

$$\|s\| \leq \frac{1}{\alpha}\|F\|_{V^*}$$

This lemma, valid for elliptic equations, can be easily extended to hyperbolic equations. For parabolic equations a similar lemma called Gronwall's lemma holds.

An elliptic equation can be expressed in terms of the elliptic differential operator as follows:

$$Lu = \sum_{|\alpha| \leq m} a_\alpha(x)\partial^\alpha u$$

$$\sum_{|\alpha| = m} a_\alpha(x)\vec{x}^\alpha \neq 0 \qquad \forall x \in \Omega \, m \in \mathbb{N}$$

A nonlinear operator is elliptic if its first-order expansion in Taylor series is an elliptic operator. The matrix associated with the elliptic operators is symmetric, real, and positive definite. An example of an elliptic operator is the Laplacian.

A parabolic equation can be expressed in terms of an elliptic operator as follows:

$$\frac{\partial u}{\partial t} = Lu$$

The solutions of a stationary parabolic equation therefore respond to elliptic operators. Equations that have this form are called backward parabolic equations:

$$\frac{\partial u}{\partial t} = -Lu$$

It is said that these equations are not well posed.

XX – Partial differential equations

The importance of partial differential equations lies in the description they can provide with respect to a huge number of physical problems: below we will mention just a few to make you understand the vastness of the subject.

A first order partial differential equation of this form:

$$\frac{\partial u}{\partial t} + \mathbf{b} \cdot \nabla u = f$$

It describes transport phenomena, such as the transmission of heat or the exchange of matter. The corresponding homogeneous equation expresses the condition that a directional derivative of the function is zero. From the method of characteristics follows the solution:

$$u(\mathbf{x}, t) = g(\mathbf{x} - t\mathbf{b})$$

If g is a generic differentiable function then we have a classical and non-weak solution. The inhomogeneous equation has the following form:

$$u(\mathbf{x}, t) = g(\mathbf{x} - \mathbf{b}t) + \int_0^t f(\mathbf{x} + (s - t)\mathbf{b}, s)\,ds$$

An elliptic equation is, for example, the Laplace equation:

$$\nabla^2 \varphi = 0$$

Physically this equation expresses Fick's law of diffusion, if the unknown is a concentration, Fourier's law for heat if the unknown is a temperature and the law of electrostatics, if the unknown is the electrostatic potential. The general solution is as follows:

$$\Phi(\mathbf{x}) = \begin{cases} -\frac{1}{2\pi} \log |\mathbf{x}| & n = 2 \\ \frac{1}{n(n-2)\alpha(n)|\mathbf{x}|^{n-2}} & n \geq 3 \end{cases}$$

Where appears the volume of the sphere of unit radius in R n-dimensional for a space having dimension greater than or equal to three.

XX – Partial differential equations

Laplace's equation is the homogeneous equation of a more general equation, called Poisson's:

$$\nabla^2 \varphi = f$$

A solution of this equation is given by:

$$\varphi(\mathbf{x}) = -\frac{1}{4\pi} \int_V \frac{f(\mathbf{x}')}{|\mathbf{x} - \mathbf{x}'|} dV$$

There is a uniqueness theorem for the Poisson equation, in particular the gradient of the solution of the equation is unique if the function is well defined on the boundary (for Dirichlet boundary conditions) or if the gradient of the function is well defined on the boundary (for Neumann boundary conditions).

Another solution of Poisson's equation can be expressed as follows:

$$u(\mathbf{x}) = \int_{\mathbf{x}'} d\mathbf{x}' G(\mathbf{x}, \mathbf{x}') f(\mathbf{x}')$$

Where G is the Green function which is defined on a generic linear differential operator:

$$L_x G(x, y) = \delta(x - y)$$

The delta function is the Dirac delta. In this way it is possible, for example, to derive the Green function for the Laplacian in three dimensions in any coordinate system (Cartesian, cylindrical or spherical).

Another elliptic equation is the Helmholtz equation:

$$\nabla^2 f + k^2 f = 0$$

This equation is an eigenvalue equation of the Laplacian and can be derived from a hyperbolic equation, called wave equation, which we will present shortly. The analytical solutions are found by separation of variables, the time part is given by:

XX – Partial differential equations

$$T(t) = D_1 e^{i\omega t} + D_2 e^{-i\omega t}$$

Where the coefficients are complex and depend on the boundary and initial conditions. The spatial part of the solution strongly depends on the boundary conditions, as in the more general wave equation.

An example of a parabolic equation is Fick's law which describes the physical mechanism of molecular diffusion:

$$\frac{\partial \phi}{\partial t} = \nabla \cdot (D \nabla \phi)$$

Where the unknown function represents the concentration and D is called the diffusion coefficient. If the concentration is stationary the equation becomes elliptical, of the form:

$$D \nabla^2 \phi + \vec{v} \cdot \nabla \phi = 0$$

If the diffusion coefficient is uniform, we have:

$$\frac{\partial \phi}{\partial t} = D \nabla^2 \phi$$

If both conditions hold, the equation coincides with Laplace's.

The heat equation is a parabolic partial differential equation which has the form:

$$u_t - \nabla^2 u = f(\bar{x}, t)$$

If f=0 we have the associated homogeneous equation. Analytically, this equation is solved by separation of variables and the solution u has the physical meaning of a temperature profile.

Another parabolic equation is the Burgers equation which models gas dynamics and traffic flows:

$$\frac{\partial u}{\partial t} + u\frac{\partial u}{\partial x} = \nu \frac{\partial^2 u}{\partial x^2}$$

XX – Partial differential equations

Where the viscosity coefficient appears, while the solution u is generally a speed. The solution of this equation passes through the method of characteristics.

A generalization of this equation is the advection equation:

$$\frac{\partial \psi}{\partial t} + \nabla \cdot (\psi \mathbf{u}) = 0.$$

The hyperbolic equation par excellence is the wave equation, also called the D'Alembert equation:

$$\nabla^2 u - \frac{1}{v^2}\frac{\partial^2 u}{\partial t^2} = 0$$

The solutions of this equation are found by separation of variables. The spatial part depends considerably on the chosen geometry, in fact in Cartesian coordinates the solutions are called plane waves, in spherical coordinates instead we have spherical harmonics and in cylindrical coordinates we have cylindrical harmonics. Furthermore, the dependence is also based on the size, the boundary conditions and the initial ones.

In the one-dimensional case, the wave equation is said for the vibrating string:

$$\frac{\partial^2 u}{\partial t^2} = a^2 \frac{\partial^2 u}{\partial x^2}$$

The general solution of the free vibrating string is:

$$u(x,t) = \frac{w_1(x-at) + w_1(x+at)}{2} + \frac{1}{2a} \cdot \int_{x-at}^{x+at} w_2(z)\,dz$$

It is also possible to derive solutions that can be developed in Fourier series.

In the two-dimensional case the wave equation represents the equation of a dynamic membrane. This equation can be generalized to different types of waves, such as acoustic waves or those of earthquake propagation obviously considering particular physical coefficients and

XX – Partial differential equations

certain boundary conditions (particularly important are the so-called absorption conditions).

Other partial differential equations important for physics are the Navier-Stokes equations for fluid dynamics. In the case of negligible viscosity they reduce to the following Euler equations:

$$
\begin{cases}
\dfrac{\partial \rho}{\partial t} + \nabla \cdot \left(\rho \, \dfrac{d\bar{r}}{dt} \right) = 0 \\[2em]
\dfrac{\partial \rho \frac{d\bar{r}}{dt}}{\partial t} + \nabla \cdot \left(\rho \, \dfrac{d\bar{r}}{dt} \times \dfrac{d\bar{r}}{dt} + p\bar{\bar{1}} \right) = 0 \\[2em]
\dfrac{\partial E}{\partial t} + \nabla \cdot \left[\dfrac{d\bar{r}}{dt} (E + p) \right] = 0
\end{cases}
$$

It must be said that for these equations, and for those that will follow, it is very difficult to find explicit analytical solutions, except in very particular cases. At this juncture, numerical methods become primary. These equations also incorporate concepts such as the conservation of some physical quantities, under the name of continuity equations.

Other partial differential equations are the Euler-Lagrange equations and those of Hamilton-Jacobi which describe classical mechanics respectively in the Lagrangian and Hamiltonian formalisms.

Fundamental partial differential equations for a physical theory are, for example, the Schrodinger equation for quantum mechanics:

$$
i\hbar \frac{\partial}{\partial t} \Psi(\mathbf{r},\, t) = -\frac{\hbar^2}{2m} \nabla^2 \Psi(\mathbf{r},\, t) + V(\mathbf{r},\, t)\Psi(\mathbf{r},\, t)
$$

And Maxwell's equations for electromagnetism:

$$
\nabla \cdot D = \rho_E
$$
$$
\nabla \cdot B = 0
$$
$$
\nabla \times E + \frac{\partial B}{\partial t} = 0
$$

185

$$\nabla \times H - \frac{\partial D}{\partial t} = J_E$$

From these equations it is possible to go back to the wave equation, in fact the physical solutions of Maxwell's equations are called electromagnetic waves.

The Euler-Tricomi equation is instead used to study transonic flows:

$$u_{xx} = x u_{yy}$$

Dym's equation is used to study soliton waves:

$$u_t = u^3 u_{xxx}.$$

The Ginzburg-Landau equation generalizes many partial differential equations to the complex case:

$$i u_t + p u_{xx} + q|u|^2 u = i\gamma u$$

A special condition of the wave equation is the propagation of so-called shock waves. Such shock waves can also propagate in fluid dynamics cases in which the equations of Euler and those of Navier-Stokes govern the modeling of the physical case. A shock wave is created when the Rankine-Hugoniot conditions are satisfied which, in the fluid dynamics case, are as follows:

$$\rho_1 u_1 = \rho_2 u_2$$

$$p_1 + \rho_1 u_1^2 = p_2 + \rho_2 u_2^2$$

$$u_1 \left(p_1 + \rho_1 e_1 + \rho_1 u_1^2/2 \right) = u_2 \left(p_2 + \rho_2 e_2 + \rho_2 u_2^2/2 \right)$$

These conditions reflect the conservation of mass, momentum and energy. The resulting equation is called the Rankine-Hugoniot equation and describes orthogonal shock waves.

For an in-depth study of all the implications of partial differential equations and shock waves, it is necessary to introduce some numerical concepts which will be explained in the chapter on numerical analysis.

XXI – Integral and integro-differential equations

XXI – INTEGRAL AND INTEGRAL-DIFFERENTIAL EQUATIONS

An integral equation is an equation that presents the unknown under the sign of integral. Actually, whenever you solve a differential equation, the solution formula is an integral equation, so we have already said a lot about such equations in previous chapters. A linear integral equation has a form like this:

$$y(x) = \lambda \int K(x,z)y(z)dz + f(x)$$

Where K(x,z) is the kernel of the equation (which can be real or complex, symmetric or antisymmetric) and f(x) is the known term. If f(x) is different from zero we speak of equations of the second kind, if it is equal to zero we speak of equations of the first kind. In integral equations, the integral is defined so we have integration extremes. If these extremes are fixed we speak of integral equation of Fredholm, if instead one of the extremes is variable in x the equation is called of Volterra.

The Fredholm operator is defined as a bounded linear operator between Banach spaces having a finite-dimensional core and con-core. Moreover, saying T a Fredholm operator (from a space X to a Y) and S a linear and bounded operator (from the space Y to that X), we have that $Id_X - ST$ and $Id_Y - TS$ are compact operators on X and on Y. The index of a Fredholm operator is defined as follows:

$$indT = \dim\ker T - codim\,ranT = \dim\ker T - \dim coker T$$

The set of Fredholm operators forms an open set in Banach space of bounded and continuous linear operators. The index of the composition of two Fredholm operators is equal to the sum of the indices of the single operators, furthermore the added Fredholm operator has the opposite index with respect to the starting one. Finally, given a Fredholm operator and a compact one, their convolution returns again a Fredholm operator having the same index as the starting one.

The tensor product between a Banach space and its dual is a complete space endowed with the following norm:

187

XXI – Integral and integro-differential equations

$$\|X\| = \inf \sum_{\{i\}} \|e_i^*\| \cdot \|e_i\|$$

The space defined by completion with this norm is denoted in this way (called B the generic Banach space) $B^* \widehat{\otimes} B$. A Fredholm kernel is an element of this projective topological space.

Each nucleus can be associated with a trace and a linear operator of canonical form:

$$trX = \sum_{\{i\}} \lambda_i e_i^* (e_i)$$

$$L_X f = \sum_{\{i\}} \lambda_i e_i^* (f) \otimes e_i$$

Moreover, every nucleus is called p-summable if the following relation holds:

$$\sum_{\{i\}} |\lambda_i|^p < \infty$$

Fredholm's theory assumes that the Fredholm nucleus is comparable to a Green function, solution of the differential equation:

$$LK(x,z) = \delta(x-z)$$

Where L is a linear differential operator. Applying this equation to Sobolev spaces and writing the previous equation as an eigenvalue equation:

$$L\psi_n(x) = \omega_n \psi_n(x)$$

An expression of the Fredholm nucleus can be derived:

$$K(x,z) = \sum_n \frac{\psi_n^*(x)\psi_n(z)}{\omega_n}$$

XXI – Integral and integro-differential equations

For the inhomogeneous Fredholm equation we can rewrite the known term in this way:

$$f(x) = -\omega y(x)$$

And the solution is given by:

$$y(x) = \frac{1}{K - \omega}\left(\frac{y}{\omega}\right)$$

Using spectral theory, the resolving operator is as follows:

$$R(\omega, x, z) = \frac{1}{K - \omega I} = \sum_n \frac{\psi_n^*(z)\psi_n(x)}{\omega_n - \omega}$$

And the solution is given by:

$$y(x) = \omega \int R(\omega, x, z) y(z) dz$$

Fredholm's theorem provides a sufficient condition for the existence of solutions of Fredholm's equations: the nucleus must be a square summable in a suitable set.

The Fredholm alternative provides a necessary and sufficient condition for the existence of the solutions: the solution must be orthogonal to the complete set of solutions of the corresponding addition equation i.e. of the Fredholm equation obtained by replacing the Fredholm kernel with its addition and each scalar with its complex conjugate.

In these cases the resolvent can be developed in a power series through the Liouville-Neumann series:

$$R(\lambda) = \frac{1}{I - \lambda \sum_{j=0}^{\infty} \lambda^j (K^j f)(x)}$$

If the nucleus is continuous, every integral Fredholm equation has a unique solution for any known term and the solution, represented by the Liouville-Neumann series, is uniformly convergent.

189

XXI – Integral and integro-differential equations

The Fredholm determinant is the following:

$$\det(I - \lambda K) = \exp\left[-\sum_n \frac{\lambda^n}{n} tr K^n \right]$$

While the determinant of the resolvent is the so-called Riemann zeta function:

$$\zeta(a) = \frac{1}{\det(I - aK)}$$

An inhomogeneous Fredholm equation of the first type having unlimited integration extrema and kernel defined thus $K(x,z)=K(xz)$ can be seen as the convolution of $K(x,z)$ and $y(z)$ therefore the solution can be written in terms of a Fourier transform or anti-Fourier transform:

$$y(t) = F_\omega^{-1}\left[\frac{F_t[g(t)](\omega)}{F_t[K(t)](\omega)} \right] = \int_{-\infty}^{\infty} \frac{F_t[g(t)](\omega)}{F_t[K(t)](\omega)} e^{2\pi i \omega t} d\omega$$

The integral equation of Volterra is solved with the same procedures as that of Fredholm, except to remember that a nucleus of Volterra has no eigenvalues.

There are other integral and integro-differential equations with which physics is scattered, in particular we can recall Maxwell's equations for electromagnetism, the compressibility equation for statistical mechanics and thermodynamics and Boltzmann's equation for physics statistics.

A fundamental field of application of integral equations concerns the calculus of variations, i.e. the search for the extremal points of the functionals.

The fundamental lemma of the calculus of variations states that given a continuous function in an open set and a continuous and continuously differentiable function in the same open set, if the following condition holds:

$$\int_a^b f(x)h(x)dx = 0$$

And the continuous and continuously differentiable function is zero in both extremes, then the other function is zero in the whole set.

Thanks to this lemma it is possible to pass from an integral version of the calculus of variations, such as Hamilton's variational principle, to the resolution of differential equations, such as those of Euler-Lagrange.

XXI – Integral and integro-differential equations

XXII – ADVANCED ALGEBRA

Advanced algebra includes abstract algebra, i.e. the study of algebraic structures, such as groups, rings and fields, category theory which tends to abstract individual algebraic structures, universal algebra which studies the common bases of all algebraic structures and the various types of algebra that can be constructed.

Referring to the next chapter for the study of algebraic structures and category theory, universal algebra defines algebra as a set A endowed with a set of operations on A. An n-ary operation on A is a function which puts relating n elements of A to a single element of A. A nullary operation is simply a constant, a unary operation is a function relating A to A.

A binary operation is said to have arity equal to two, i.e. it is a function of the Cartesian product AxA which refers to A. A binary operation is also called the law of composition and an algebraic structure equipped with a binary operation is called magma, the simplest algebraic structure. Other more complex algebraic structures are defined by two or more binary operations. Sum and product are examples of two binary operations, while subtraction is not if it refers to the set of natural numbers.

Operations with higher arity can also be infinite operations. Each operation can be subject to different axioms, among which we recall the properties of associativity, distributivity, existence of the identity element, of the neutral one or of the inverse one.

A graded algebra is an algebra defined on particular structures, such as a field or a commutative ring. Linear algebra is the algebra underlying linear systems, vector spaces, matrix mathematics, and analytic geometry. The algebra related to combinatorics, with the definition of probability and related properties, is called sigma-algebra and is the typical algebra defined on sets. The study of algorithms and information and recursive structures is called computational algebra. An algebra in which the internal unary operation is given by the normal derivative is called a differential algebra. An algebra involving elementary logical operators and truth tables is called Boolean algebra.

An algebra on a field K is called K-algebra and is thus defined as a vector space A on the field K endowed with a binary operation which is a bilinear form, ie which satisfies the properties of bilinear distributivity and bilinear associativity of a scalar. K is called the base field of algebra A and the binary operation is called product, although in reality it is not always the usual product operation. Two algebras defined on the same field are said to be isomorphic if and only if there is a bijective linear map connecting them. Every K-algebra can be specified up to isomorphisms by giving an n-th dimension and specifying the n structure coefficients.

We define commutative algebra as that part of abstract algebra which studies commutative algebraic structures, in the same way a non-commutative algebra deals with non-commutative algebraic structures. With similar concepts one can define an associative algebra.

Examples of associative algebras are given of the algebra of square matrices defined on a field (and with the product operation given by the normal multiplication between matrices), the algebra (which is also commutative) of all polynomials on the field K.

An associative algebra over real numbers or complex numbers that is also a Banach space is called a Banach algebra. The product operation defined on this algebra is a continuous function, furthermore the algebra is normed if the space is normed. A Banach algebra is said to be unitary if it has an identity element for the product operation whose norm is equal to one and is said to be commutative if the product is commutative. The set of real numbers and that of complex numbers are Banach algebras if the norm of the absolute value is defined, in the same way the sets of real or complex square matrices are Banach algebras by associating a norm to these matrices.

A Banach algebra on a complex field endowed with an involution property which sends an element into its conjugate and which enjoys this property:

$$\forall x \in A \Rightarrow \left\| x^* x \right\| = \left\| x \right\|^2$$

It's called C^* algebra. Given two C^* algebras, an algebraic homomorphism is a homomorphism which respects the involution property. The algebra of square matrices over a complex field becomes an C^* algebra if it has the classical norm. If an C^* algebra admits an algebraic tensor product with any other C^* algebra, then it is said to be nuclear. A generalization of an C^* algebra is given by B^* algebra: in fact in this case the involution operation respects the properties of associativity, isometry and anti-commutativity.

An associative algebra having a quadratic form Q on a vector space V is called Clifford algebra Cl(V,Q). Once an nth basis of the space V is defined, the dimension of the Clifford algebra is equal to:

$$\dim Cl(V,Q) = 2^n$$

A not necessarily associative algebra whose product is commutative and satisfies the following Jordan identity is called a Jordan algebra:

$$(xy)(xx) = x(y(xx))$$

Given any associative algebra, but not one with characteristic equal to two, a Jordan algebra can be defined simply by using the addition operation in the vector space.

An associative algebra defined for any partially ordered set is called an incidence algebra. The identity element for the product of an incidence algebra is the Kronecker delta, while the zeta function is the unit constant.

A Lie algebra defined on a vector space and on a field has a binary operator called the Lie product which is bilinear, antisymmetric, nilpotent and satisfies the Jacobi identity:

$$[[x, y], z] + [[z, x], y] + [[y, z], x] = 0$$

A Lie algebra is said to be Abelian if the Lie product yields the zero vector for all x and y. The three-dimensional Euclidean space with the classical vector product is a Lie algebra. An associative algebra can be transformed into a Lie algebra by defining the Lie product as the commutator:

$$[x, y] = xy - yx$$

Vector field algebras defined on differentiable manifolds are Lie algebras.

A complex Lie algebra defined as an extension of the vector field of complex polynomials on the unit circle is called a Virasoro algebra.

An algebra over a field for which the product is alternative is called an alternative algebra. The alternative product is defined as follows:

$$(xx)y = x(xy)$$
$$y(xx) = (yx)x$$

Every associative algebra is alternative, but the opposite is not necessarily the case. We define associative algebras on powers algebras for which the following product relations hold:

$$\forall m,n \in N \Rightarrow x^m * x^n = x^{m+n}$$

Of particular importance is the sequence of Caylery-Dickson algebras on real fields. We can include the dimensional algebra of complexes (which is commutative and associative), the algebra of quaternions which is associative, that of octonions which is alternative and that of sedenions which is associative over powers. We will define in the next chapter the algebraic structures related to these important objects of advanced mathematics.

An algebra is of division if there are multiplicative inverses while it is quadratic if the decomposition of the square according to the sum of elements of the base field and of the invertible element holds. Up to isomorphisms, the only quadratic algebras on the reals are the real numbers, the complex ones, the quaternions and the octonions. An algebra with two products involving a commutative algebra and a Lie algebra is called a Poisson algebra.

Given a topological space (X,T), the Borel algebra of X with respect to T is the smallest σ-algebra containing the topology T. Given two topological spaces and a continuous function connecting them, then this function is said to be measurable compared to the Borel algebra. The measurable functions in this algebra are called Borel's, as are the sets (sometimes also called Borel's) and the measure is precisely that of Borel. Two borelian spaces are isomorphic if there exists a measurable bijective function with an inverse that is also measurable. The most used Borel algebra is the one defined on real numbers and Euclidean spaces, in particular as regards the definition of probability.

A superalgebra over a commutative ring or field K is a direct-sum decomposition with bilinear multiplication such that we have:

$$A = A_0 \oplus A_1 \mid A \times A \to A \mid A_i A_j \subseteq A_{i+j}$$

196

XXII – Advanced Algebra

In theoretical physics, we define supersymmetric algebras, i.e. those that incorporate the concept of supersymmetry between particles. There are supersymmetric extensions of both the Lie algebra and the Virasoro algebra. Similarly, there are supercommutative algebras which extend the concept of commutator.

Noteworthy is the Poincaré superalgebra, a supersymmetric extension of the Poincaré algebra, itself defined as the Lie algebra of the Poincaré group.

XXII – Advanced Algebra

XXIII – ALGEBRAIC STRUCTURES

A mathematical structure defined on a set consists of objects that characterize the set, such as measure, topology, metric, ordering, and algebra.

An algebraic structure is a support set of the structure endowed with operations that can be nullary, unary and binary and which have specific properties. In this chapter we will give a detailed list of the main algebraic structures and their properties. We define substructure as a subset of an algebraic structure which is closed under the operations defined in it.

A class is a generic collection of objects that can be identified. All sets are classes, while classes that are not sets are called proper classes.

A morphism is a process that transforms one structure into another while keeping some of its properties unchanged. Each morphism starts from a domain and connects it to a codomain, furthermore for each object there is a morphism called identity which transforms a structure into itself by means of composition with the same morphism.

A homomorphism is an application between two algebraic structures of the same type which preserves the operations defined therein. An injective homomorphism is called a monomorphism, a surjective one is called an epimorphism, and a bijective one is called an isomorphism. If the domain and the codomain coincide, then every homomorphism is called an endomorphism (an example is given by the identity function) and every isomorphism is called an automorphism.

If a domain has ordering properties, then there exists an order isomorphism, called isotonia, which maintains the ordering property also in the codomain. We will see that particular isomorphisms can be defined in every algebraic structure, for now we recall that an isomorphism between vector spaces is a bijective linear transformation and one between topological spaces is a bijective map called homeomorphism.

An automorphism of a set is a permutation of the elements of the set; an automorphism of a vector space is an invertible linear operator on the space. We can distinguish internal automorphisms deriving from conjugations between elements of the same object and external automorphisms.

The study of morphisms and classes is done in detail in category theory. By category we mean a mathematical entity endowed with a class $Ob(C)$

XXIII – Algebraic structures

whose elements are called objects, with a class Mor(C) whose elements are called morphisms and with a binary operation, called composition of morphisms, which satisfies the property association and the existence of identity.

A category is said to be small if the object class is a set. Categories are sets, functions, homomorphisms, vector spaces, measurable spaces, topological spaces and differentiable manifolds.

The maps between the categories that preserve their structures are called functors. Within the functors, one can distinguish the covariant ones from the contravariant ones.

The Euler characteristic is an integer describing the nature of the algebraic structure. It was initially introduced for polyhedra like this:

$$\chi = V - S + F,$$

Where V, S and F are the number of vertices, edges and faces of the polyhedron. For all simply connected polyhedra this value is equal to 2. The concept can be extended to topological spaces and algebraic structures by recalling that the Euler characteristic of disjoint sets is equal to the sum of the Euler characteristics of the single sets and that the Euler characteristic of the product of spaces is equal to the product of the Euler characteristics of the individual spaces. For example, the straight line, the plane and every Euclidean space have unitary Euler characteristic as well as the projective plane, while the sphere has Euler characteristic equal to 2, the Klein bottle, the Mobius strip and the torus have such value that it is null.

In differential geometry there is the Gauss-Bonnet theorem according to which, for a two-dimensional Riemannian manifold it is compact, the following holds:

$$\int_M K \, dA + \int_{\partial M} k_g \, ds = 2\pi\chi(M)$$

Where the Gaussian curvature, the geodesic curvature of the boundary and the Euler characteristic of the manifold appear.

The first algebraic structure that we present is that of a group, a set provided with a binary operation which enjoys the associative properties, of existence of the neutral element and of the inverse one. If

XXIII – Algebraic structures

the commutative property also holds, the group is said to be commutative or abelian. The cardinality of the group is called order and if it is finite, then the group is said to be finite. The importance of groups derives from the definition of a theory of groups which is fundamental for the understanding of contemporary physics.

For example, integers with the sum operation are an abelian group, permutations of a set are a group with the function composition operation, a vector space is an abelian group with respect to the sum of vectors. Particular groups can be defined on matrices such as the orthogonal group, formed by orthogonal square matrices, and the general linear group formed by invertible square matrices; We will explore some of these aspects below.

We define the direct product of two groups as the Cartesian product between them. There are other types of product between groups, including free and semi-direct products that are based on other rules and which define other product groups.

We say action of a group G on a set A, a function such that:

$$e \cdot a = a \quad \forall a \in A;$$

$$g \cdot (h \cdot a) = (gh) \cdot a \quad \forall g, h \in G, \ a \in A.$$

The center of a group is the following subset:

$$C := \{c \,|\, c * g = g * c \ \forall g \in G\}.$$

The centralizer of an element of a group is the following set:

$$Z(g) := \{h \in G \,|\, g * h = h * g\}.$$

Two elements are inverse if:

$$a * b = b * a = 1$$

Two elements of a group are conjugate if:

$$h^{-1} * a * h = b$$

A class formed only by conjugate elements is called a conjugate class.

XXIII – Algebraic structures

A subset H of a group G is a subgroup if it is a group with the operation defined on G; a subgroup of a finite group is finite and one of an abelian group is abelian.

A subset of a given set that is endowed with an algebraic structure is called a set of generators if all the elements of the set can be obtained through combinations of operations defined therein. For a group, the generator set is the smallest subset that contains that subset.

An ordered group is a group with order structure.

The symmetric group is the group formed by the set of permutations of its elements. The order of the symmetric group is n! and this group is not abelian if n>2.

The aforementioned general linear group, the group of all invertible square matrices over a field K, is denoted by GL(n,K). The special linear group is the subgroup of such matrices which have unitary determinant and is denoted by SL(n,K). Such groups are never abelian for n>1, the diagonal matrices are a subgroup of GL(n,R) which is a differentiable manifold.

The orthogonal group of degree n over a field K is the group of orthogonal matrices and is denoted O(n,K). If K is the set of real numbers, then this group represents the isometries of Euclidean space. The orthogonal matrices with unitary determinant form a subgroup denoted by SO(n), called the special orthogonal group which is also the group of rotations of the space. The orthogonal group is a subgroup of the group GL(n,K) and is a differentiable manifold, but it is not connected.

A cyclic group is defined as a group generated by a single element, called the generator of the group. A cyclic group is always abelian while every finitely generated abelian group is cyclic. Integers are an example of a cyclic group of infinite order. The direct product of two cyclic groups has order equal to the product of the orders of the cyclic groups and is cyclic if and only if these orders are coprime. Every finite group of first order is a cyclic group. A dicyclic group is a non-abelian group of order 4n that arises from the extension of a cyclic group with another cyclic group of order 2.

We call dihedral group that group of order 2n formed by the isometries of the plane which leave the regular polygons of n sides unchanged. This group is not abelian.

Given a group G and a subgroup K, this subgroup is normal if:

$$gK = Kg$$

XXIII – Algebraic structures

In an abelian group, every subgroup is normal; the kernel of a homomorphism is a normal subgroup of the group; every subgroup of order 2 is normal.

A simple group is a nontrivial group whose only normal subgroups are the trivial subgroup and the group itself. A cyclic group is simple if and only if its order is a prime number.

We call a Dedekind group that group in which every subspace is normal and a Hamiltonian group a non-abelian group in which every subgroup is normal.

Given a group G and its normal subgroup H, the quotient group of the equivalence classes is defined as:

$$G/H = \{[g] \mid g \in G\}$$

The extension of a group is a group in which there is a normal subgroup that is isomorphic to the starting group.

A group is said to be nilpotent if the chain of normal subgroups thus defined ends in a finite way:

$$\{e\} = Z_0 \subseteq Z_1 \subseteq \ldots \subseteq Z_n = G,$$

Where each individual subgroup is defined as a quotient group having a given center.

A group is said to be solvable if there exists a chain of subgroups where each of them is normal to the next and their quotient group is abelian.

A group is said to be free if there exists a subset such that it is possible to write, in a unique way, each element of the group as a product of a finite number of elements of the subsets and its inverses.

A Lie group is a group having a structure of differentiable manifold such that a morphism is a differentiable homomorphism. These groups are categories together with their morphisms.

A group presentation is the list of group generators and group relationships. If the set of generators is finite the presentation is said to be finitely generated, if the set of relations is finite it is said to be finitely related. Each finished group has a finished presentation.

The kernel of a homomorphism between groups is a normal subgroup, while abelian groups have an abelian homomorphism.

XXIII – Algebraic structures

Particularly important in physics is the group of quaternions, i.e. the group formed by the eight elements (1, -1, i, -i, j, -j, k, -k). The following relationships hold:

$$i^2 = j^2 = k^2 = -1$$

$$ij = k, \ ji = -k$$

$$ik = -j, \ ki = j$$

$$jk = i, \ kj = -i$$

This group is not abelian but is Hamiltonian and is isomorphic to the group of invertible matrices with complex values.

A non-associative extension of this group is that of the octonions which forms a non-associative 8-dimensional algebra on the field of real numbers; this algebra is the only finite-dimensional non-associative one definable on real numbers. Actually, the octonions do not form a group but a quasigroup (we will see this definition shortly).

A further extension is that of sedenions, a 16-dimensional algebra on the field of real numbers. As with octonions, the binary operation is neither associative nor commutative.

There are several fundamental theorems in group theory.

Given a topological space X union of two open sets A and B, such that the sets and their intersection are arc-connected, Van Kampen's theorem states that, considered a basis point in the intersection set, the fundamental group of the space topological is given by the following product:

$$\pi(X, x_0) = \pi(A, x_0) *_{\pi(A \cap B, x_0)} \pi(B, x_0)$$

If A and B are simply connected, then so is X.

Sylow's first theorem states that a finite group G admits a subgroup of order equal to a prime number raised to an integer such that their power is a divisor of the order of the group.

If the order of a finite group can be expressed as the product of the power mentioned above and a coprime number at the base of the power, then Sylow's second theorem states that all subgroups of order equal to the power are conjugate.

XXIII – Algebraic structures

Sylow's third theorem, having assumptions the same as those of the second, states that the number of subgroups of order equal to the power is divisible by the power base.

The first isomorphism theorem states that the kernel of a homomorphism between groups is a normal subgroup and the quotient group is isomorphic to the codomain of the homomorphism.

The second isomorphism theorem states that given two subgroups of a group, one of which is normal, then their product subset is a subgroup of the group. Furthermore, the normal subgroup is also normal in the product subset. The isomorphism induced by the map on the codomain of the quotient group between the product subset and the normal subgroup is called canonical.

The third isomorphism theorem states that given two normal subgroups, one of which is contained in the other, then the following canonical isomorphism holds on quotient groups:

$$(G/N)/(H/N) \cong G/H.$$

Lagrange's theorem states that a subgroup of a finite group has order which is a number divisor of the order of the group. From this it follows that a group that has a prime number of elements is cyclic.

Cauchy's theorem states that given a finite group of order n and a prime number that divides n, then there exists in the group elements of order equal to that prime number.

We now introduce other types of algebraic structures.

A semigroup is a set endowed with an associative binary operation; analogous considerations apply to what was done for groups, above all for the character of finiteness and commutativity. A semigroup with a neutral element is called a monoid: it goes without saying that every group is also a monoid.

Given a commutative semigroup with an equivalence relation on the sum per component, the Grothendieck group of this semigroup is the quotient set and is abelian.

A set having a partial associative function and a total inversion function which is always defined is called a groupoid.

A quasigroup is an algebraic structure similar to that of a group where, however, the associative and existence properties of the neutral element are not required. The binary operation is defined as follows:

a*x=b, so x=a\b
y*a=b, so y=b/a

and it is called, respectively, left division and right division. For example, integers with the operation of subtraction form a quasigroup. The deletion property exists in a quasigroup.

A quasigroup with a neutral element is called a loop, so each element of the loop has a unique left inverse and a unique right inverse; moreover, an associative loop is a group. Inside the loop it is possible to define the left translations, given by the multiplication "to the left" and the right translations. All translations of a loop generate a group. A Moufang loop satisfies the juxtaposition identity which is a weak version of associativity:

$$(a \cdot b) \cdot (c \cdot a) = (a \cdot (b \cdot c)) \cdot a$$

We say left-loop an algebraic structure similar to the loop in which only the binary operation "to the left" is valid:

a*x=b, so x=a\b

Each loop is a left-loop. Left-loops can be constructed from sections of quotient groups.

A monoid is an algebraic structure with a single binary operation, called a product. This structure is closed with respect to the binary operation, has the associative property and the neutral element exists. As already mentioned, a monoid is a unitary semigroup and a group is a monoid with an inverse element.

We define lattice as a partially ordered set; it is an algebraic structure equipped with two binary operations which are commutative, associative and for which the laws of absorption and idempotence hold. For example, the natural numbers with the usual order relation are a lattice. The lattices with their homomorphisms form a category. A lattice is said to be bounded if it has a maximum and a minimum, whereas it is said to be complete if each of its subsets has the lower and the upper bounds. A lattice is distributive if the distributive laws on the two binary operations hold, while it is said to be modular if the distributivity holds for only one of the binary operations. Furthermore, a complete lattice which is continuous as an ordered lattice is called continuous and a complete lattice which is algebraic as an ordered lattice is called algebraic. An ordered subset of a lattice is called a sublattice.

A semilattice has the same properties as a lattice but defined on a single binary operation, called meeting, and not on two.

A magma is an algebraic structure with a single binary operation that satisfies only the closure property. For what has been said, groups, semigroups, quasigroups, loops, left-loops, monoids, lattices, semilattices are all particular magmas. A magma can be characterized in various ways, for example on the basis of the properties of commutativity, idempotence, distributivity, mediality, alternativeity and so on.

Other algebraic structures are more refined than those presented so far.

A ring is defined as a set with two binary operations, called sum and product, such that the set and the sum operation are an abelian group with a neutral element given by zero while the set and the product operation are a semigroup with neutral element given by the unit. Furthermore, the product is distributive with respect to the sum. In the rings the binomial expansion holds; furthermore it is not required that the product be commutative, while the sum must be. A ring in which the product is also commutative is called a commutative ring; every cyclic group is a commutative ring. A subring is a subgroup of a ring that is closed with respect to the product. An element of a ring is invertible if there is another element such that the product of the two elements (both the left and right) equals unity. The direct product of two rings is their Cartesian product. Examples of rings are spaces of matrices and polynomials.

An element of a ring is said to be irreducible if it is not a unit and cannot be written as a product of two elements that are non-units.

We define an ideal subset of a ring that is closed with respect to the interior sum and product for each element of the ring. In particular, the subset for which the right product of the two elements is part of the ideal is called right ideal, and the one for which this property holds for the left product is called left ideal. An ideal that is both right and left is said to be bilateral; if the ring is commutative all ideals are bilateral. An ideal is called proper if it is a proper subset of the ring, ie if and only if it does not contain the unity of the ring. The sum and product of ideals are:

$$I + J := \{a + b \mid a \in I, b \in J\}$$

$$IJ := \{a_1 b_1 + \ldots + a_n b_n \mid a_i \in I, b_i \in J, i = 1, 2, \ldots, n; \text{ per } n = 1, 2, \ldots\},$$

The intersection of two ideals is an ideal, the union need not be.
An ideal Q of a ring A is primary if, in the quotient ring A/Q, the set of divisors of zero coincides with that of nilpotent elements. The expression of that ideal as a finite intersection of primary ideals is called the primary decomposition of an ideal. The ideal generated by a single element is called the principal ideal.
A ring is called an integrity domain if it is commutative and if the product's vanishing law holds

$$a \cdot b = 0 \Rightarrow a = 0 \quad \text{oppure} \quad b = 0$$

The set of integers is an integrity domain, while a non-commutative ring can never be an integrity domain. A domain of integrity in which every ideal is principal is called a principal ideal domain. In such domains, an element is prime if and only if it is irreducible.
A unique factorization domain is an integrity domain in which every non-invertible element is a product of prime elements. In these domains, the notions of prime element and irreducible element coincide. An integrity domain is said to be Euclidean if it is a commutative ring in which it is possible to perform a Euclidean division operation. A Euclidean domain is a principal ideal domain.
The characteristic of a ring is the smallest non-zero natural number such that the element given by the sum of unity n times is equal to zero. If this minimum value does not exist then the characteristic is zero by definition. The characteristic of a ring is the least common multiple of the characteristics of its elements; furthermore if the ring is an integrity domain, each non-zero element has the same characteristic therefore the characteristic of an integrity domain is equal to zero or a prime number. A ring with a finite number of elements always has a non-zero characteristic.
A ring extension is a pair of rings, one of which is contained within the other. A homomorphism between rings is a function between two rings that preserves the two operations of addition and product. The class of all rings with their homomorphisms is a category. The kernel of a ring homomorphism is an ideal.

XXIII – Algebraic structures

A quasi-ring is an algebraic structure similar to a ring but in which the sum is not required to be commutative and that the distributive law of the product with respect to the sum holds on both sides. A quasi-ring in which the distributive law holds to the left is called left. If the quasi-ring contains the element that is neutral with respect to the product, it is called a quasi-ring with unity.

A semi-ring is an algebraic structure in which the binary operations of sum and product are associative, the distributive property of the product with respect to the sum holds, the neutral element for the sum exists and is unique and the null element of the product exists. From what has been said, each ring is also a semi-ring.

A body is a set endowed with two binary operations, called sum and product, for which the set and the sum operation are an abelian group with neutral element, the set and the product operation are a group with unitary element, the product is distributive with respect to the sum. For example, the set of quaternions is a body.

A field is a set endowed with two binary operations, called sum and product, for which the set and the sum operation are an abelian group with neutral element, the private set of this neutral element and the product operation are a abelian group with unitary element, the product is distributive with respect to the sum. A field is a commutative ring in which every nonzero element has an inverse and is also a commutative body with respect to the product.

Examples of fields are algebraic numbers, the set of complex numbers, the set of real numbers and that of rational numbers; moreover, every finite integrity domain is a field.

Typically the product of fields is not a field, so RxR is a ring but not a field; the quaternion group is also not a field.

On a field, the only ideals are the null element and the field itself, therefore any non-zero homomorphism between fields is injective. The fields are integrity domains, Euclidean domains, and unique factorization domains. A field is said to be finite if it has finite cardinality.

The closed subset with respect to the operations of sum and product, which is itself a field, is called a subfield. The intersection of all subfields is called the prime or fundamental subfield.

A field such that each element of it is algebraic in the field to be extended is said to be an algebraic extension of a field. The maximal algebraic extension of a field is its algebraic closure, therefore a field is algebraically closed if it coincides with its algebraic closure.

XXIII – Algebraic structures

The normal extension is the one generated by the complete factorization of a set of polynomials; the separable extension is the one generated by the roots of separable polynomials. A field for which every finite extension is separable is called a perfect field. All fields having characteristic zero and all finite fields are perfect.

An extension field generated by the complete factorization of a polynomial is called splitting field. A field with total order is called ordered, while it is called numerical if it is an algebraic extension of the field of rational numbers and is called quadratic if this extension is of degree two. Finally, a field is called cyclotomic if it is an extension, generated by the root of unity, of the field of rational numbers.

As we have seen, it is possible to associate a field with a field algebra, ie a vector space equipped with a binary operation. A homomorphism between two algebras over a field is a function such that the properties of additivity, multiplication by a scalar and separation of the product hold. If this function is bijective then we are witnessing an isomorphism between algebras.

Algebraic topology is that part of mathematics which applies the concepts of advanced algebra and algebraic structures to study topological spaces. In particular, the low-dimensional topology studies the topological spaces of one, two, three or four dimensions and therefore applied to the straight line, the circumference, the surfaces, the manifolds (in this context the Poincaré conjecture was recently proved). Of particular importance is algebraic geometry, i.e. the study of the geometry of algebraic varieties.

XXIV – GALOIS THEORY

Galois theory is a part of abstract algebra and historically arises from the attempt to solve the Abel-Ruffini theorem, according to which there is no solution formula for the roots of a generic polynomial equation of fifth degree or higher using algebraic operations elementary. Galois theory answers this and other classical questions, such as the impossibility of constructing a square with an area equal to that of a circle.

Given an extension E of a field F, an automorphism which fixes the elements of F is called F-automorphism:

$$\psi : E \rightarrow E \,|\, \forall x \in F, \psi(x) = x$$

The F-automorphisms of the extension form a group called the Galois group which is denoted by:

$$G = Gal(E/F)$$

The splitting field of a polynomial defined on a field F is defined as an extension of the field in which the polynomial is factorized and the roots generate the extension itself. Each field has a unique splitting field, up to isomorphisms.

If there exists an algebraically closed field K which contains the field F, then there exists a unique splitting field of the polynomial contained in the field K.

A polynomial is said to be separable if each of its irreducible factors has distinct roots in the splitting field. All irreducible polynomials that have a zero in a separable extension are separable, so all polynomials having coefficients defined over perfect fields are separable.

Given a separable polynomial with coefficients in a field, the Galois group of the polynomial is the one defined on the extension given by the splitting field of the polynomial in the field.

The Galois group defined on the fields of complex and real numbers Gal(C/R) has two elements given by identity and complex conjugation. The Galois group defined on the fields of real and rational numbers Gal(R/Q) is trivial having the identity as its only element. The Galois group defined on fields of complex and rational numbers is infinite.

XXIV – Galois theory

If F is a finite field with positive characteristic p, then it is an extension of a field and we have that:

$$Gal(F, F_p) = C_n = \langle f \rangle$$

In this case the Galois group is the cyclic group of nth order and f is a Frobenius-defined endomorphism.

An extension E/F is Galois if the fixed field of the Galois group Gal(E/F) coincides with the base field F. In particular, if E is a field and G is a finite group of automorphisms of E, then the E/F extension is Galois.

Moreover, a finite extension is Galois if and only it is normal and separable or E is the splitting field of a separable polynomial with coefficients in F or if the degree of the extension is equal to the order of the automorphism group of E/ f.

An infinite extension is Galois if and only if it is normal and separable or E is the splitting field of a family of separable polynomials with coefficients in F.

Given an extension of E/F fields with associated Galois group G=Gal(E/F) we define two Galois connections as follows:

1) For each field L between F and E, i(L)=Gal(E/L) is the subgroup of the automorphisms of E that leave the elements of L fixed.

2) For each subgroup H of G, j(H) is the field between F and E consisting of the elements of E which are left fixed by all the automorphisms of H.

The fundamental theorem of Galois theory in the finite case states that the Galois connections thus defined are inverse of each other and therefore there is a bijection between the set of fields between F and E and the subgroups of the Galois group g.

For the infinite case, this theorem states that a bijection is generated between the set of fields between F and E and the set of subgroups of G which are closed with respect to a particular topology, called Krull.

We define a solvable group as a group that has an abelian normal series, i.e. there is a chain of subgroups defined in this way:

$$\{e\} \subseteq H_1 \subseteq \ldots \subseteq H_n = G$$

212

Where e is the neutral element, each subgroup is normal to the next one and the quotient given by one subgroup and the previous one is abelian. If G is a finite group the quotients are also cyclic. It is proved that a polynomial is solvable over a field F with characteristic zero if and only if its Galois group over F is solvable.

Through the definition of solvable Galois groups and the fundamental theorem of Galois theory, the Abel-Ruffini theorem can be proved.

It is also possible to solve the inverse Galois problem, that is to determine which groups G are Galois groups of some Galois extension on a fixed field F. If such an extension exists, G is said to be feasible on F. There is not yet a general solution to the inverse problem, but only solutions in particular cases. For finite fields, the Galois group is always cyclic and therefore the inverse problem is easy to solve. Furthermore, every abelian group is the Galois group of some extension of the field of rational numbers. With the exception of the Mathieu group, all simple groups can be realized as Galois groups on the field of rational numbers. Finally, all solvable groups are Galois groups of an extension of the field of rational numbers.

If the field on which to realize the Galois group is not fixed, the inverse Galois problem has a trivial resolution, exploiting the fundamental theorem of Galois theory and Cayley's theorem.

Galois theory is a starting point for other theories, including monodromy studies and Kummer's theory.

The monodromy group of a polynomial is a normal subgroup of the Galois group, furthermore an algebraic function on the whole complex plane is monodromous if and only if it is rational.

We define Kummer extension as an extension of fields L/K such that L is generated on K by a root of the polynomial $x^n - a$ with n>1 and a belonging to K and such that K contains n distinct roots of $x^n - 1$. These extensions are Galois extensions with a cyclic Galois group.

Kummer's theory studies the inverse case ie, if K contains n distinct n-th roots of unity, then any cyclic extension of K of degree n is obtained by adding an n-th root.

XXIV – Galois theory

XXV – COMBINATORY GEOMETRY

Combinatorial geometry studies finite or countable sets of objects that satisfy the properties of membership and order. In the first instance it can be said that this discipline of mathematics generalizes the concepts of combinatorics in relation to particular geometric structures, such as graphs, trees and drawings. Furthermore, combinatorial geometry is part of discrete mathematics.

A graph G is an ordered pair of sets V and E, where V is the set of nodes and E the set of edges such that the elements of E are pairs of elements of V. Two nodes joined by an edge are called endpoints of the arc and the arc is identified with the pair of numbers of its extremes.

An arc having two coincident extremes is called a loop, while multiple arcs joining the same extremes generate a multi-arc.

A graph without loops and multi-edges is called simple, otherwise it is called multi-graph. The graph obtained by eliminating all loops and replacing each multi-edge with a single edge having the same endpoints is called a skeleton of a graph.

The number of edges existing on a node is called the degree of the node. The minimum and maximum degree of a graph are, respectively, the degree of the node with the minimum number of subsistent edges and the degree of the node with the maximum number of subsistent edges.

A graph is said to be regular when the maximum and minimum degree coincide and, in this case, the graph is said to be regular of order equal to the degree. A graph is said to be planar if, in the plane, the edges intersect only at the nodes. A planar graph is said to be maximal if, with the addition of any new node, it is no longer planar. Every planar graph without loops is tetrapartite, i.e. it respects the four color theorem.

A graph without edges is called a null graph, in particular the graph which contains neither edges nor nodes is null.

If a path exists between two nodes, they are said to be connected. A graph is connected if all of its nodes are connected. The adjacency of a node is the set of nodes connected to the reference node. In a connected graph, the eccentricity of a node is the maximum distance from one node to another.

The connection relation between the nodes is an equivalence relation and, in the single equivalence classes, subgraphs can be defined. An isolated node is a node that is not connected to any other node and that node has degree zero. A connected planar graph drawn without boundary intersections has Euler characteristic equal to two.

A graph defined with a set of nodes W, a subset of V, is called an induced subgraph with respect to the starting graph.

A directed graph is characterized by directed arcs, that is by arcs that have a direction: a node reached at the entrance by an directed arc is called head, one reached at the exit is called tail. In a directed graph there is an order relation between the nodes. In an undirected graph there are no directed edges and the relationship between the edges is symmetric. A simple graph has no directed edges.

An undirected graph is complete if any two of its nodes are adjacent. Calling N the number of nodes, the number of edges of a complete graph is equal to:

$$\frac{N(N-1)}{2}$$

The maximum cardinality of a complete subgraph of a graph is called the density of the graph. It is called a clique of an undirected graph, a complete subgraph such that all nodes of the clique are pairwise adjacent and no other complete subgraph contains the clique. An ordering of the nodes of an undirected graph is said to be perfect if the intersection between the adjacency and the ordered nodes is a complete subgraph.

In a directed graph, a parent of a node is a node such that the directed pair between it and the node belongs to the edge set. Similarly, a child of a node is a node such that the directed pair between the node and the child belongs to the arc set. A node that has no parents is called a root.

A path of given length is an ordered sequence of nodes and a sequence of edges connecting them. The first and last nodes are called endpoints of the path. A path with pairwise distinct sides is called a path. A closed path is called a cycle; a loop is said to be simple if it does not pass through the same node twice. In an undirected graph, the tour of the graph is a cycle that passes through each node only once.

A chain is a sequence of nodes and a sequence of edges connecting them where the ordering of the sequence does not matter. A chain is called cyclic if the initial node coincides with the final one; moreover, for an undirected graph, the concept of chain and that of path are equivalent. Also in an undirected graph, a simple path or cycle has a chord if there is an arc between two non-consecutive nodes of the cycle.

An undirected graph is said to be triangulated if every cycle of length greater than or equal to four has a chord.

A forest is a graph in which each node has, at most, one parent. The nodes without parents are called roots, those without children are the leaves, while the sequences of arcs are called branches. It goes without saying that a forest has no cycles.

A graph is said to be bipartite if the set of nodes can be divided into two subsets such that each node of one subset is connected only to a node of the other subset. A bipartite graph therefore has the set of nodes given by the union of two subsets. All undirected and noncyclic graphs are bipartite as are cyclic graphs but with an even number of nodes. The union of bipartite graphs gives rise to other bipartite graphs. A bipartite graph is convex if there is an ordering in one of the two subsets that respects the adjacency property. If the adjacency property is respected by the orderings in both subsets, the graph is said to be biconvex. A bipartite graph is said to be complete if there are all edges connecting the elements of one subset with those of the other.

A dual graph of a planar graph is a graph that has a node for each region of the planar graph and each edge for each edge of the planar graph. The dual of a planar graph is planar. The duality property is invertible if the starting graph is also connected.

A graph in which the relationship between the number of nodes and the number of arcs is exponential with a negative exponent is called a scale-free network. A scale-free network is represented, for example, by the Internet and by the models on which social networks are based.

A random graph is a graph generated by a random variable having a given probability distribution. Random graphs give rise to random networks.

A tree is an undirected graph in which any two nodes are connected by one and only one path. The tree is therefore a particular planar, bipartite, connected and acyclic graph; moreover it is also a connected forest: consequently a forest is a disjoint union of trees.

The tree is a connected graph that has the minimum number of nodes to maintain the connection property. The level of a root is zero, that of a generic node is one plus the level of the parent; the height of a tree is the maximum among the levels of all its nodes.

A binary tree is a tree in which each parent has at most two children. For a binary tree the height is given by $\log_2 k$ where k is the number of leaves. The path length of a binary tree is the sum of the node levels.

XXV – Combinatorial geometry

Every tree with a number greater than or equal to two nodes has at least two leaves. Every tree with n nodes has n-1 edges. Furthermore, there is only one path between any pair of nodes.

A rooted tree is said to be rooted, a tree is ordered if it is rooted and the children of each root are fully ordered.

A spanning tree of a connected and undirected graph is a tree containing all the vertices of the graph but only a subset of the edges, in particular only those necessary for the connection between all vertices with a single path.

There are various computational algorithms for combinatorial geometry, in particular Kruskal's algorithm calculates spanning trees of minimum total weight, Dijistra's algorithm searches for shortest paths in a cyclic graph, Boruvka's algorithm defines the minimum spanning tree of a graph in which the weight of each pair of arcs is distinct.

Combinatorial geometry also deals with design theory. A drawing is an ordered pair of sets V and B, where V is a set of positive cardinality of elements called points and B is a set of parts (called blocks) of V, each with a smaller cardinality than that of V. For each drawing an incidence matrix can be associated; from the study of these matrices the main properties of the drawings are obtained.

XXVI – DISCRETE MATHEMATICS

Discrete mathematics deals with the study of discrete quantities, over all countable sets. Some parts of discrete mathematics have already been covered in this textbook, such as combinatorics, discrete transforms and combinatorial geometry; other sectors will be addressed in the following chapters such as number theory, set theory, statistics and stochastic processes applied to discrete variables.

A topological space has a discrete topology when all its subsets are open or, equivalently, when all its subsets are closed or when all its points are open. The discrete topology is the one with the greatest degree of finesse of all topologies, the opposite is the trivial topology.

A metric space having a discrete metric has a definite distance equal to zero if the elements coincide and equal to one if the elements are different. The discrete topology is therefore metrizable and satisfies all separation axioms. A discrete space is totally disconnected, homogeneous and is compact if and only if it is finite. Up to homeomorphisms, discrete spaces are classified by their cardinality: it follows that every countable discrete space is homeomorphic to the set of relative numbers.

Discrete geometry is concerned with the study of geometric objects by determining their discrete and combinatorial properties.

A result of discrete geometry is Pick's theorem: in a simple polygon whose vertices have integer coordinates, called i the number of integer coordinate points inside the polygon and p the number of integer coordinate points on the perimeter of the polygon, the area of the polygon is given by Pick's formula:

$$A = i + \frac{p}{2} - 1$$

Another result of discrete geometry is the formulation (and demonstration) of Kepler's conjecture according to which, given spheres in three-dimensional Euclidean space, there is no way to arrange them with an average density higher than that obtained using cubic geometry a centered faces or the hexagonal one. Another aspect of discrete geometry is the resolution of triangulation problems.

219

XXVI – Discrete mathematics

Thanks to discrete mathematics it is possible to generalize many geometric properties of solids, in particular of polyhedra by defining the combinatorial structure as the set of its vertices, its edges and its faces and their respective incidence relationships. In addition, it is also possible to define its metric structure, i.e. in terms of discrete metric spaces. It can be seen how a rotation around an axis of symmetry or a translation leaves the metric and combinatorial structures unaltered, while a homothety transforms only the metric structure.

Generalizing to the n-dimensional Euclidean space R, the analog of the polygon in the plane and of the polyhedron in space is defined as the n-dimensional polytope. As with most Euclidean geometry, the study focuses on convex polytopes; in particular, the convex closure of a finite set of points is called V-polytope, while H-polytope is the intersection of half-spaces of a bounded n-dimensional space R. The dimension of a convex polytope is the dimension of the minimum subspace that contains it, while two convex polytopes are said to be affine isomorphic if there is a bijective affine transformation between the two spaces that contain them.

XXVII – ADVANCED STATISTICS

Advanced statistics can be divided into two broad categories: descriptive statistics and inferential statistics. Descriptive statistics summarizes and studies all statistical criteria and classifications, especially using concepts such as indices of expected value, variance and covariance. Inferential statistics, starting from combinatorics and probability theory, comes to define random variables, their probability distributions, estimation theory and hypothesis testing; within inferential statistics there is also Bayesian inference which we will discuss later.

A random or random variable is a measurable function on a sample space in which a probability measure is defined. This variable can have values in R, and therefore have one dimension, or have more dimensions and in this case we speak of multivariate random variables.

Each random variable X can be associated with a distribution or probability law which assigns to each subset of possible values of X the probability that the random variable takes on value in that subset and is defined as follows:

$$P_X(A) := P(X \in A) = \nu(X^{-1}(A))$$

Where the last relation is the probability measure defined on the sample space.

If the random variable is discrete then the discrete probability function is defined as follows:

$$p(x) = P(X = x)$$

While if it is continuous, the probability density function is given by:

$$P(X \in A) = \int_A p_X(x) \, dx$$

Where A is a subset of the sample space and the integral is intended according to Lebesgue.

XXVII – Advanced statistics

For multivariate random variables the following extension for the probability density function holds:

$$P(X \in A) = \int_A p_{X_1,\ldots,X_n}(x_1, \ldots, x_n) \, d\, x_1 \ldots d\, x_n$$

This is called the joint probability density function. On the other hand, the probability density of a single component, called the marginal density, is defined as follows:

$$p_X(x) = \int_{\mathbb{R}} p_{X,Y}(x,y) \, d\, y$$

In the case of multivariate discrete variables, the following definitions apply for joint and marginal probability functions:

$$p_X(x_1, x_2, \ldots, x_n) = P((X_1 = x_1) \cap (X_2 = x_2) \cap \ldots \cap (X_n = x_n))$$

$$p_X(t) = P(X = t, Y \in \mathbb{R}) = \sum_{y \in R_Y} P(X = t, Y = y)$$

Instead, it is called a distribution function, a non-decreasing function, continuous to the right and with the following properties:

$$F(x) \geq 0, \quad \forall x$$

$$\lim_{x \to +\infty} F(x) = 1$$

$$\lim_{x \to -\infty} F(x) = 0$$

Such that one has that:

$$F(x) = P(X \leq x).$$

The relations between the distribution function and the probability function are given by the following formulas, respectively in the continuous and in the discrete case:

$$F(x) = \int_{-\infty}^{x} f(u)\,du$$

$$F(x) = \sum_{x_i \leq x} p(x_i)$$

The following probability function (continuous case and discrete case) is called conditional distribution:

$$f_Y(y \mid X = x) = \frac{f_{X,Y}(x,y)}{f_X(x)},$$

$$p_Y(y \mid X = x) = P(Y = y \mid X = x) = \frac{P(X = x \cap Y = y)}{P(X = x)}.$$

If two random variables are independent then the denominators of these relations are unitary.

The expected value of random variables is defined as follows in the discrete and continuous cases:

$$\mathbb{E}[X] = \sum_{i=1}^{\infty} x_i\, p_i$$

$$\mathbb{E}[X] = \int_{-\infty}^{\infty} x f(x)\,dx$$

The expected value of a constant is the constant itself, furthermore the expected value is linear and the expected value of the sum of the independent random variables is equal to the sum of the expected values of the single random variables (this result, however, does not require the condition of independence as necessary). Furthermore, the expected value is monotonic, i.e. if one random variable is greater than another, then its expected value will also be greater than that of the other.

XXVII – Advanced statistics

The conditional expected value of a random variable is the expected value with respect to a conditional probability distribution and can be expressed as follows, respectively in the discrete and continuous cases:

$$E[X|Y=y] = \sum_x x \frac{P(X=x \wedge Y=y)}{P(Y=y)}$$

$$E[X|Z] = E[X|\sigma(Z)]$$

We define variance as the following quantity:

$$\sigma^2(x) = E\left[\left(x - E[x]\right)^2\right] = E[x^2] - E[x]^2$$

The variance is never negative and is zero only when the variable assumes a value with probability equal to the certain event.
The variance has the following property:

$$\sigma^2(ax+b) = a^2\sigma^2(x)$$

Furthermore, for two independent random variables:

$$\sigma^2(x+y) = \sigma^2(x) + \sigma^2(y)$$

$$\sigma^2(x-y) = \sigma^2(x+(-y)) = \sigma^2(x) + \sigma^2(-y) = \sigma^2(x) + \sigma^2(y)$$

The variance of discrete and continuous random variables is given by:

$$\sigma^2(x) = \sum_{y \in X} (y - E[x])^2 P(x=y)$$

$$\sigma^2(x) = \int_X (y - E[x])^2 f(y) dy$$

The measure of the independence of two random variables is given by the covariance:

$$\mathrm{cov}(X,Y) = E\left[(X - E[X])(Y - E[Y])\right]$$

Which can be expressed like this:

$$\mathrm{cov}(X,Y) = E[XY] - E[X]E[Y]$$

Two independent random variables always have zero covariance (if the covariance is zero, however, the variables can also be dependent). The covariance has the following properties:

$$\mathrm{cov}(X,Y) = \mathrm{cov}(Y,X)$$

$$\mathrm{cov}(aX + b, Y) = a\,\mathrm{cov}(X,Y)$$

$$\mathrm{cov}(X + Y, Z) = \mathrm{cov}(X,Z) + \mathrm{cov}(Y,Z)$$

The variance is given by the covariance applied to the same random variable. In general, the variance of the sum of two non-independent random variables is given by:

$$\sigma^2(x + y) = \sigma^2(x) + \sigma^2(y) + 2\sigma^2(x,y)$$

Where the covariance appears in the last term.
The law of total variance states that:

$$\sigma^2(x) = \mathbb{E}[\sigma^2(x|y)] + \sigma^2(\mathbb{E}[x|y])$$

From this law we can obtain a value for the conditional variance:

$$\sigma^2(x|y) = \mathbb{E}[(x - \mathbb{E}[x|y])^2|y]$$

For multivariate random variables, a covariance matrix can be expressed as follows:

$$\sigma_{ij} = \frac{1}{n}\sum_{h=1}^{n}(x_{hi} - \mu_j)^2$$

XXVII – Advanced statistics

Where the second term in the squaring is the mean. The values on the diagonal of this matrix, i.e. those where i=j, represent the variances.
We define the simple moment of origin m and order k of a random variable (discrete case and continuous case):

$$\mu_{m,k} = \sum_{i=1}^{n}(x_i - m)^k p_i$$

$$\mu_{m,k} = \int_{-\infty}^{+\infty}(x - m)^k p_X(x)dx$$

If the origin m is equal to the mean, this moment is called the central moment. The following expression for the discrete and continuous cases is called the moment generating function:

$$g(t) = E[e^{tX}] = \sum_{i=1}^{n} p_i e^{tX_i}$$

$$g(t) = E[e^{tX}] = \int_{-\infty}^{\infty} e^{tx} f_X(x)dx$$

From this function we obtain the simple moments which are the derivatives of order k calculated at the point t=0. Given n independent random variables and defining X as their sum, then it holds:

$$g(t; X) = \prod_{i=1}^{n} g(t; X_i)$$

The Pearson correlation index of two random variables is the ratio of their covariance to the product of the square roots of their variances:

$$\rho_{xy} = \frac{\sigma_{xy}}{\sigma_x \sigma_y}$$

It is valid that:

226

$$-1 \leq \rho_{xy} \leq 1$$

If this index is positive, the variables are said to be directly correlated; if it is negative, inversely correlated, if it is zero, uncorrelated.
In statistics, some fundamental inequalities hold. Cebichev's inequality states that, given a random variable of known mean and variance, we have that:

$$\Pr\left(|X - \mu| \geq \lambda \cdot \sigma\right) \leq \frac{1}{\lambda^2}$$

Markov's inequality holds for non-negative random variables:

$$\Pr\left(X \geq \alpha\right) \leq \frac{E[X]}{\alpha}$$

Given n independent random variables, each of which is limited in the minimum and maximum values between two values and that S is the sum of these variables, the Hoeffding inequality holds (for t>0):

$$P(S - E[S] \geq t) \leq e^{-\frac{2t^2}{\sum (b_i - a_i)^2}}$$

Jensen's inequality states that, given a convex function, the following holds:

$$\varphi\left(\mathbb{E}\{X\}\right) \leq \mathbb{E}\{\varphi(X)\}.$$

The convergence of random variables has several meanings in statistics. A sequence of random variables with a given distribution function is said to converge in distribution (or in law) to the random variable X with distribution function F if the following limit exists finitely, for every point where F is continuous:

$$\lim_{n \to \infty} F_n(x) = F(x)$$

The convergence in distribution is indicated as follows:

$$X_n \xrightarrow{d} X$$

For any continuous and bounded function the convergence in distribution is equivalent to:

$$\lim_{n \to \infty} E[g(X_n)] = E[g(X)]$$

A sequence of random variables converges in probability to the random variable X if:

$$\lim_{n \to \infty} P(|X_n - X| \geq \varepsilon) = 0$$

And it is indicated by:

$$X_n \xrightarrow{p} X$$

Convergence in probability implies convergence in distribution.
A sequence of random variables converges almost everywhere to the random variable X if:

$$P(\lim_{n \to \infty} X_n = X) = 1$$

And it is indicated by:

$$X_n \xrightarrow{q.o.} X$$

Convergence almost everywhere implies that in probability.
A sequence of random variables converges on the r-th mean to the random variable X if:

$$\lim_{n \to \infty} E(|X_n - X|^r) = 0$$

If r=1 it is said to converge on the mean, if r=2 on the quadratic mean. Convergence in the r-th mean with positive r implies convergence in probability and convergence almost everywhere (the latter up to subsequences).

We are now going to list the main characterizations of discrete and continuous random variables and the probability distributions related to them.

The discrete uniform distribution is the distribution that gives the elements of a finite set the same probability of occurring. Given a and b as the extremes of the progression of the n elements, we can write the probability density, the distribution function, the expected value, the variance and the moment generating function as:

$$\frac{1}{n}$$

$$\frac{i}{n}$$

$$\frac{a+b}{2}$$

$$\frac{(a-b)^2}{12}\frac{n+1}{n-1}=\frac{n^2-1}{12}$$

$$\frac{1}{n}e^{at}\frac{1-e^{\frac{n}{n-1}(b-a)t}}{1-e^{\frac{1}{n-1}(b-a)t}}$$

The Bernoulli distribution is a distribution of a discrete random variable that can take on only two values p and q, where q=1-p and is denoted by B(p). The density and the distribution function are given by:

$$P(0)=q$$
$$P(1)=p$$
$$P(0)=q$$
$$P(1)=1$$

The expected value is equal to p, the variance equal to the product of p and q. The moment generating function is given by:

$$q + pe^t$$

The sum of n independent random variables each of which has the Bernoulli distribution gives rise to the binomial distribution. The density function, the expected value, the variance and the moment generating function are:

$$P(k) \; = \; P(X_1 + X_2 + \ldots + X_n = k) \; = \; \binom{n}{k} p^k q^{n-k}$$

$$E[S_n] \; = \; \sum_{i=1}^{n} E[X_i] \; = \; nE[X] \; = \; np$$

$$\mathrm{Var}(S_n) \; = \; \sum_{i=1}^{n} \mathrm{Var}(X_i) \; = \; n\mathrm{Var}(X) \; = \; npq$$

$$g(S_n, t) \; = \; \prod_{i=1}^{n} g(X_i, t) \; = \; g(X, t)^n \; = \; (q + pe^t)^n$$

The generalization of the binomial distribution to the case of several variables is given by the multinomial distribution, whose density function is given by:

$$P(n_1, \ldots, n_s) = \binom{n}{n_1, \ldots, n_s} \prod_i p_i^{n_i} = \frac{n!}{n_1! \cdots n_s!} p_1^{n_1} \cdots p_s^{n_s}$$

The covariance matrix is given by:

$$m_{i,i} = n\,\mathrm{Var}(X_i) = np_i(1 - p_i)$$
$$m_{i,j} = n\,\mathrm{cov}(X_i, X_j) = -np_i p_j$$

The discrete probability distribution that models the probability for the number of events that occur successively and independently in a given time interval, knowing that on average a given quantity occurs, is given by the Poisson distribution, whose density is:

$$P(n) = e^{-\lambda} \frac{\lambda^n}{n!}$$

Where n is a natural number. The expected value, the variance and the moment generating function are given respectively by:

$$E[Y] = \sum ne^{-\lambda}\frac{\lambda^n}{n!} = \lambda e^{-\lambda}\sum \frac{\lambda^{n-1}}{(n-1)!} = \lambda$$

$$\text{Var}(Y) = E[Y^2] - E[Y]^2 = \sum n^2 e^{-\lambda}\frac{\lambda^n}{n!} - \lambda^2 = \lambda^2 + \lambda - \lambda^2 = \lambda$$

$$g(t,Y) = E[e^{tY}] = e^{-\lambda}\sum \frac{\lambda^n e^{tn}}{n!} = e^{-\lambda}e^{\lambda e^t} = e^{\lambda(e^t-1)}$$

A binomial distribution converges in law to a Poisson distribution. Given two Poisson distributions each with a reference parameter, their sum follows a Poisson distribution having a reference parameter equal to the sum of the parameters of the single distributions. Furthermore, the conditional distribution of this sum distribution is equal to the binomial distribution having parameter equal to the ratio between the parameters.

The discrete probability distribution over the natural numbers that follow a geometric progression is called the geometric distribution. The density function is given by:

$$\Pr(Y = k) = (1-p)^k p$$

The distribution function, the expected value, the variance and the moment generating function are:

$$P(T \leqslant k) = 1 - P(T \geqslant k+1) = 1 - q^{k+1}$$

$$E[T] = \sum_k kpq^k = \frac{1}{p}$$

$$\text{Var}(T) = E[T^2] - E[T]^2 = \frac{q}{p^2}$$

$$g(T,t) \ = \ E[e^{tT}] \ = \ p\sum_{k} q^k e^{kt} = \frac{p}{1 - qe^t}$$

The geometric distribution of parameter q describes the number of failures preceding the first success in a Bernoulli distribution. Furthermore, this distribution is devoid of memory, i.e.:

$$P(T = m + n|T > m) = P(T = n)$$

The hypergeometric distribution models the random variable that matters, for r distinct elements drawn equally probably from a set of cardinality n, those that are in a subset of cardinality h. The probability of obtaining k elements is given by:

$$P(k) = \frac{\binom{h}{k}\binom{n-h}{r-k}}{\binom{n}{r}}$$

The expected value and the variance are given by:

$$E[N] = \sum_{b\in B} E[X_b] = \frac{rh}{n}$$

$$\mathrm{Var}(N) = \sum_{i} \mathrm{Var}(X_i) + \sum_{i\neq j} \mathrm{cov}(X_i, X_j) = \frac{r(n-r)\,h(n-h)}{n^2(n-1)}$$

The hypergeometric distribution with r=1 coincides with the Bernoulli distribution having as parameter the ratio between h and n. For functions of several variables it is possible to generalize the hypergeometric distribution into a multivariate hypergeometric distribution.

We define a degenerate distribution as a discrete distribution in which the probability distribution is concentrated in a single value. The density function and the distribution function are unitary in this value and zero in every other value. The variance is always zero and the expected value is equal to the reference value.

XXVII – Advanced statistics

The Pascal distribution describes the number of failures preceding the nth success in a Bernoulli distribution of parameter p. The density function is given by:

$$P(k) = \binom{-n}{k} p^n (-q)^k$$

According to this expression, the Pascal distribution is also called negative binomial. The expected value, the variance and the moment generating function are given by:

$$E[T_n] = nE[T] = n\frac{q}{p}$$

$$\text{Var}(T_n) = n\,\text{Var}(T) = n\frac{q}{p^2}$$

$$g_{T_n}(t) = g_T(t)^n = \left(\frac{p}{1 - qe^t}\right)^n$$

Pascal's distribution describes the sum of n independent random variables having identical geometric distribution of parameter q.
The Skellam distribution describes the difference of two independent random variables both having a Poisson distribution. The density function is given by:

$$P(n) = e^{-(\lambda_1 + \lambda_2)} \left(\frac{\lambda_1}{\lambda_2}\right)^{\frac{n}{2}} I_{|n|}(2\sqrt{\lambda_1 \lambda_2})$$

Where I is the Bessel function of the first kind. The expected value, the variance and the moment generating function are given by:

$$E[Y] = E[X_1] - E[X_2] = \lambda_1 - \lambda_2$$

$$\text{Var}(Y) = m_2(Y) = s = \lambda_1 + \lambda_2$$

$$g_Y(t) = g_{X_1}(t)g_{X_2}(-t) = e^{\lambda_1 e^t + \lambda_2 e^{-t} - (\lambda_1 + \lambda_2)}$$

A Panjer distribution is a discrete distribution on the natural numbers defined by recursion:

$$P(n) = p_k$$

$$p_k = (a + \frac{b}{k})p_{k-1}$$

On the basis of the values of a and b, one can have degenerate, binomial, Pascal, Poisson distributions or have no probability distribution. In particular, if a+b=0 we have the degenerate distribution, if this sum is positive and a<0 we have the binomial one, if the sum is positive and a=0 we have the Poisson one, if the sum is positive and a>0 we have has that of Pascal, if the sum is negative there are no probability distributions. The expected value and the variance are:

$$E[X] = \frac{a+b}{1-a}$$

$$\mathrm{Var}(X) = \frac{a+b}{(1-a)^2}$$

The Benford distribution is given by:

$$P(n) = \log_{10}(n+1) - \log_{10}(n) = \log_{10}(1 + 1/n)$$

And it's important in number theory.
At the continuous level, the continuous uniform distribution generalizes the discrete uniform distribution to a continuous set in which the probability distribution is uniform. The probability density, the expected value, the variance, the moment generating function are given by:

$$f(x) = \frac{1}{b-a}$$

$$E[X] = \frac{1}{2}, \qquad E[Y] = a + (b-a)E[X] = \frac{a+b}{2}$$

$$\mathrm{Var}(X) = \frac{1}{12}, \qquad \mathrm{Var}(Y) = (a-b)^2\mathrm{Var}(X) = \frac{(a-b)^2}{12}$$

$$g_X(t) = E[e^{tX}] = \frac{e^t - 1}{t}, \qquad g_Y(t) = e^{at}g_X((b-a)t) = \frac{e^{bt} - e^{at}}{bt - at}$$

The continuous distribution of paramount importance is the normal or Gaussian distribution, whose probability density is given by the Gaussian function:

$$f(x) = \frac{1}{\sqrt{2\pi\sigma^2}} \, e^{-\frac{(x-\mu)^2}{2\sigma^2}} \quad \text{con} \quad x \in \mathbb{R}$$

With this notation, the expected value, the variance and the moment generating function are given by:

$$E[X] = \mu$$

$$\mathrm{Var}[X] = \sigma^2$$

$$M_X(x) = \exp\left(\mu x + \frac{\sigma^2 x^2}{2}\right)$$

The general notation of the normal distribution is as follows $N(\mu;\sigma^2)$. The normal distribution is an even function with axis of symmetry given by x=E[x]. A particular case occurs when the mean is zero and the variance is unitary with the standard normal distribution N(0,1) whose probability density is given by:

$$f(x) = \frac{1}{\sqrt{2\pi}} e^{-\frac{x^2}{2}}$$

Having the following graph:

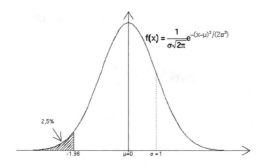

$$f(x) = \frac{1}{\sigma\sqrt{2\pi}} e^{-(x-\mu)^2/(2\sigma^2)}$$

The sum of n independent normal random variables gives rise to another normal distribution whose expected value is a linear combination of the expected values of the single random variables and variance equal to the quadratic combination.

The central Lindeberg-Levy limit theorem states that, given a sequence of independent and identically distributed random variables having finite expected value and variance, the random variable:

$$S_n = \frac{\bar{x} - \mu}{\sigma} \sqrt{n}$$

It converges in distribution to N(0,1). Basically, for n large enough, every continuous distribution that satisfies the above hypotheses converges to the normal one.

The strong law of large numbers states that, given a sequence of independent random variables having finite expected value and variance, the sample mean of that sequence almost certainly converges to the common mean.

The weak law of large numbers states that, given a sequence of independent random variables having the same expected value and the same variance, the sample mean converges in probability to the common mean.

The continuous exponential distribution has the following probability function:

$$f(x) = \lambda e^{-\lambda x}$$

The expected value, the variance and the moment generating function are given by:

$$E[X] = 1/\lambda$$

$$\text{Var}(X) = 1/\lambda^2$$

$$g_X(t) = \left(1 - \frac{t}{\lambda}\right)^{-1}$$

From the distribution function we can see that this distribution has no memory:

$$F(x) = P(X \leqslant x) = 1 - e^{-\lambda x}$$

The exponential distribution generalizes the geometric discrete distribution to the continuous case.
The Cauchy distribution has the following probability function:

$$f_{(x_0,y_0)}(x) = \frac{1}{\pi} \frac{y_0^2}{(x - x_0)^2 + y_0^2}$$

This distribution has no moment generating function and neither expected value nor variance and therefore the central limit theorem does not apply to it. The ratio of two independent random variables each with the standard normal distribution N(0,1) follows the Cauchy distribution of parameters 0 and 1.
The gamma distribution has the following probability function:

$$f(x) = \frac{1}{\theta^k \Gamma(k)} x^{k-1} e^{-\frac{x}{\theta}} = \frac{\beta^\alpha}{\Gamma(\alpha)} x^{\alpha-1} e^{-\beta x}$$

Where is the Euler gamma function:

$$\Gamma(k) = \int_0^\infty t^{k-1} e^{-t} dt$$

The expected value and the variance are given by:

$$E[X] = k\theta$$

$$\mathrm{Var}(X) = k\theta^2$$

The sum of n independent random variables each with gamma distribution of parameters ke theta has a gamma distribution equal to the sum of the ke theta parameters.

If k is a natural number, the gamma distribution assumes a simplified form called the Erlang distribution. If k=1 we have the exponential distribution.

The beta distribution is defined on the unitary interval [0,1] and has a probability function given by:

$$f(x) = \frac{x^{\alpha-1}(1-x)^{\beta-1}}{\mathrm{B}(\alpha, \beta)}$$

Where B is the Euler beta function:

$$\mathrm{B}(\alpha, \beta) = \int_0^1 x^{\alpha-1}(1-x)^{\beta-1}dx$$

The expected value and the variance are:

$$E[X] = \frac{\alpha}{\alpha + \beta}$$

$$\mathrm{Var}(X) = \frac{\alpha\beta}{(\alpha + \beta)^2(\alpha + \beta + 1)}$$

The sum of independent random variables having the standard normal distribution gives rise to the chi-squared probability distribution. The number of independent random variables that are added together is called the degree of freedom and is denoted by the letter k. The probability function is:

XXVII – Advanced statistics

$$f_k(x) = \frac{1}{2^{k/2}\Gamma(k/2)} x^{k/2-1} e^{-x/2}$$

Where does Euler's gamma function appear? It can be seen that the chi-squared distribution is a special case of the gamma distribution:

$$\Gamma(\tfrac{k}{2}, \tfrac{1}{2}) = \chi^2(k)$$

So the expected value and the variance are:

$$\mathbb{E}[x] = k$$

$$\sigma^2(x^2) = 2k$$

Given n independent random variables and standard normals such that the following relationship holds:

$$\sum_{i=1}^{n} U_i^2 = Q_1 + \cdots + Q_k$$

And defined n as the sum of the ranks of the various Qs:

$$r_i + \cdots + r_k = n$$

Cochran's theorem states that the various Q are independent and distributed as chi-squared variables each with respective r degrees of freedom.

The ratio between two random variables, the first with a normal distribution and the second with a chi-squared distribution, gives rise to another continuous distribution called Student's t. This distribution is symmetric and has a probability function:

$$f(t) = \frac{\Gamma(\frac{n+1}{2})}{\sqrt{n\pi}\Gamma(\frac{n}{2})} \left(1 + \frac{t^2}{n}\right)^{-(n+1)/2} = \frac{1}{\sqrt{n}B(\frac{1}{2}, \frac{n}{2})} \left(1 + \frac{t^2}{n}\right)^{-(n+1)/2}$$

The expected value is zero, the variance is given by (for n>2):

XXVII – Advanced statistics

$$\text{Var}(T) = \frac{n}{n-2}$$

If n=1 this distribution corresponds to the Cauchy distribution of parameters 0 and 1.

The relationship between two random variables having chi-squared distributions is described by a continuous distribution called Fisher-Snedecor. The probability density function is:

$$f(x) = \frac{1}{B(\frac{m}{2}, \frac{n}{2})} \frac{1}{x} \left(\frac{m^m n^n x^m}{(mx+n)^{m+n}} \right)^{\frac{1}{2}}$$

The expected value and the variance are:

$$E[F] = \frac{n}{n-2} \text{ per } n > 2;$$

$$\text{Var}(X) = \frac{2n^2(m+n-2)}{m(n-2)^2(n-4)} \text{ per } n > 4;$$

The Dirichlet distribution is a multinomial continuous probability distribution which has the following probability density function:

$$f(x_1, x_2, \ldots, x_k | \alpha_1, \alpha_2, \ldots, \alpha_k) = \frac{\Gamma(\alpha)}{\Gamma(\alpha_1)\Gamma(\alpha_2)\ldots\Gamma(\alpha_k)} x_1^{\alpha_1 - 1} x_2^{\alpha_2 - 1} \ldots x_k^{\alpha_k - 1},$$

The expected value and the variance are:

$$E(X_i) = \frac{\alpha_i}{\alpha},$$

$$Var(X_i) = \frac{(\alpha - \alpha_i)\alpha_i}{\alpha^2(\alpha + 1)}.$$

If k=2 then each X is distributed as a beta function.

Statistical inference falls into two broad areas of interest: estimation theory and hypothesis testing. At the basis of both areas is sampling understood as the choice of the sample of the statistical population: it can be random, probabilistic, reasoned or convenient. The sampling methods depend on the probability distribution and on the random variables just described.

The estimation theory allows to estimate parameters starting from measured data through a deterministic function called estimator. There are various properties that characterize the quality of an estimator including correctness, consistency, efficiency, sufficiency, and completeness.

A correct estimator is a function that has an expected value equal to the quantity to be estimated, vice versa it is called biased. The difference between the expected value of the estimator and that of the sample is called bias, if this difference is zero as the sample tends to infinity then the estimator is said to be asymptotically correct.

Given a random variable X of unknown parameter Y, an estimator T(X) is sufficient for Y if the conditional probability distribution of X given by T(X) does not depend on Y.

An estimator for the parameter Y is said to be weakly consistent if, as the sample size approaches infinity, it converges in probability to the value of Y. If, on the other hand, it almost certainly converges, then it is said to be strong in the consistent sense. A sufficient condition for weak consistency is that the estimator is asymptotically correct and that we have at the same time:

$$\lim_{n \to \infty} \mathrm{var}\left(T_n(X)\right) = 0$$

We define Fisher information as the variance of the logarithmic derivative associated with a given likelihood function (we will define the concept of likelihood shortly).

$$\mathcal{I}(\vartheta) = \mathrm{E}\left[\left(\frac{\partial}{\partial \vartheta} \ln f(X; \vartheta)\right)^2\right]$$

This quantity is additive for independent random variables. The Fisher information of a sufficient statistic is the same as that contained in the whole sample. In the case of multivariate distributions we have:

$$\mathcal{I}(\vartheta)_{m,n} = \mathrm{E}\left[\frac{\partial}{\partial\vartheta_m}\ln f(X;\boldsymbol{\theta})\frac{\partial}{\partial\vartheta_n}\ln f(X;\boldsymbol{\theta})\right]$$

The Cramer-Rao inequality states that the variance of an unbiased estimator is thus related to the Fisher information:

$$\mathrm{var}\left(\hat{\vartheta}\right) \geq \frac{1}{\mathcal{I}(\vartheta)} = \frac{1}{\mathrm{E}\left[\left(\frac{\partial}{\partial\vartheta}\ln f(X;\vartheta)\right)^2\right]}$$

In the multivariate case it becomes:

$$\mathrm{cov}_{\boldsymbol{\theta}}(\boldsymbol{T}(X)) \geq \mathcal{I}(\boldsymbol{\theta})^{-1}$$

The efficiency of an unbiased estimator is defined as follows:

$$e(T) = \frac{1/\mathcal{I}(\vartheta)}{\mathrm{var}(T)}$$

From the Cramer-Rao inequality it follows that the efficiency for a correct estimator is less than or equal to 1. An estimator is said to be efficient if its variance reaches the lower bound of the Cramer-Rao inequality and it is said to be asymptotically efficient if this value is reached as a limit. The relative efficiency between two estimators is given by:

$$e(T_1, T_2, \vartheta) = \frac{\mathrm{E}\left[(T_1 - \vartheta)^2\right]}{\mathrm{E}\left[(T_2 - \vartheta)^2\right]}$$

The probability associated with the sample is given by the following probability distribution:

$$P(\{x_i\}_{i=1}^n \,|\vartheta) = \mathcal{L}_D(\vartheta|\,\{x_i\}_{i=1}^n)$$

To estimate the parameter, the available data x that make up the sample can be used. The maximum likelihood method searches for the most likely value of this parameter, i.e. that maximizes the probability of having obtained the sample. In this case the function appearing on the second side of the previous relation is called the likelihood function and the estimator is called maximum likelihood:

$$\hat{\vartheta} = \arg \max_{\vartheta \in \Theta} \mathcal{L}_D \left(\vartheta | x_1, \ldots, x_n \right)$$

One can choose such estimators to be correct or asymptotically correct. Furthermore, the maximum likelihood estimator may not necessarily be unique for a given probability distribution. Given a maximum likelihood estimator for one parameter, then the maximum likelihood estimator for another parameter that functionally depends on the first is given by applying the same function, provided it is bijective. Maximum likelihood estimators do not reach the lower bound for the variance established by the Cramer-Rao inequality.

The likelihood function is a conditional probability function defined as follows:

$$\mathcal{L}(b|A) = \alpha P(A|B = b)$$

Another method for finding estimators is the so-called method of moments. Using this method, an estimator satisfies the conditions of one or more sample moments. It must be said that the maximum likelihood estimators are more efficient than the moments method estimators. A typical condition of the method of moments is the following:

$$E\left[f\left(x_i; \vartheta_0 \right) \right] = 0$$

Another estimation method, fundamental for linear regression, is the least squares method which allows the identification of trend lines starting from experimental data so that the sum of the squares of the distances between these data and the estimated ones is minimal. The estimators for the slope and intercept are given by:

$$\hat{\beta}_1 = \frac{\sum_{i=1}^{n} (X_i - \bar{X})(Y_i - \bar{Y})}{\sum_{i=1}^{n} (X_i - \bar{X})^2} = \frac{s_{XY}}{s_X^2}$$

$$\hat{\beta}_0 = \bar{Y} - \hat{\beta}_1\bar{X}$$

Where we have, in the case of simple linear regression:

$$Y_i = \beta_0 + \beta_1 X_i + u_i$$

While for the multivariate case we have:

$$Y_i = \beta_0 + \beta_1 X_{1i} + \beta_2 X_{2i} + \cdots + \beta_k X_{ki} + u_i$$

In both cases the statistical error, given by the last parameter u, has zero conditional mean.
The Rao-Blackwell estimator is defined as the conditional expected value of an estimator with respect to a sufficient statistic:

$$E[\delta(X)|T(X)]$$

The Rao-Blackwell theorem states the standard deviation of a Rao-Blackwell estimator is less than or equal to that of the original estimator:

$$E[(\delta_1(X) - \vartheta)^2] \le E[(\delta(X) - \vartheta)^2]$$

So the Rao-Blackwell estimator represents an improvement on the initial estimator.
An estimator is complete if for each measurable function:

$$E(g(s(X))) = 0 \Rightarrow \forall\, \vartheta, P_\vartheta(g(s(X)) = 0) = 1$$

The Lehmann-Scheffé theorem states that a correct, complete and sufficient estimator is a minimum variance correct estimator, i.e.:

$$\text{var}(\delta(X_1, X_2, \ldots, X_n)) \le \text{var}(\tilde{\delta}(X_1, X_2, \ldots, X_n))$$

The Gauss-Markov theorem states that, in a linear regression model having zero expected value error, the best corrected linear estimator is the least squares estimator.
A Bayes estimator is a function that minimizes the expected value of the posterior probability of a function, called loss. Given a parameter

XXVII – Advanced statistics

with known prior probability distribution and called L a loss function, then the Bayes risk of the estimator is given by:

$$E_\pi\{L(\theta, \delta)\}$$

The Bayes estimator is the one that minimizes this value. Under suitable conditions, for a large sample, the Bayes estimator is asymptotically unbiased and converges in distribution to the normal distribution with zero expected value and variance equal to the inverse of the Fisher information, therefore it is also asymptotically efficient.

The second sector of statistical inference is the verification of hypotheses following a statistical test which can be parametric or non-parametric. A test that can be applied in the presence of a given probability distribution of the data is called parametric, otherwise the test is called non-parametric.

A statistical test involves a statistical error that can be divided into two categories: the first type error is given by rejecting the hypothesis when it is true, the second type is given by accepting the hypothesis when it is false. This hypothesis is called the null hypothesis or zero hypothesis.

The Neyman-Pearson fundamental lemma states that, given two simple hypotheses, the ratio of likelihood functions that reject the first hypothesis for the second hypothesis is given by:

$$\Lambda(x) := \frac{L(\theta_0 \mid x)}{L(\theta_1 \mid x)} \leq k \text{ con } P(\Lambda(X) \leq k|H_0) = \alpha$$

And it represents the most powerful hypothesis test. If this holds for any value of the parameter, then the test is said to be uniformly more powerful.

If we assume the null hypothesis to be true, then the p-value indicates the probability of getting a result equal to the one observed. It indicates the minimum level of significance for which the null hypothesis is rejected.

The most common parametric tests are given by the Student test where the data distribution is the Student's t or the Fisher test where the data distribution is the Fisher-Snedecor one or the zeta test where the data distribution is a standard normal N(0,1).

In a parametric test it is of fundamental importance to define the confidence interval, ie the range of plausible values for the parameter to be estimated or tested. The Neyman setting for the confidence interval asserts that it is a set of parameters for which the null hypothesis is accepted. The confidence level of the interval is given by 1 minus the significance level of the test.

There are many nonparametric tests, let's list some of particular importance.

The binomial test is applied to Bernoulli statistical samples and the probabilities are calculated when the null hypothesis is true.

A test for two dependent samples and to understand the evolution of the situation is the sign test which takes into consideration the difference (positive or negative) of the two samples based on the individual parameters.

Given a binary sequence, the sequence test is performed to verify the independence of the data. The number of repeated sequences in a sequence of length N is a normal random variable of expected value and variance given by:

$$\mu = 1 + 2\frac{N^+N^-}{N}$$

$$\sigma^2 = \frac{(\mu - 1)(\mu - 2)}{N - 1}$$

Where the quotes + and − indicate the positive or negative symbols of the sequence.

Budne's test tests the null hypothesis that two data sets come from two random variables having the same distribution.

The Kolmogorov-Smirnov test tests the shape of sampling distributions and is a nonparametric alternative to the Student test.

The Kruskal-Wallis test tests the medians of different samples for equality.

Pearson's chi-squared test is applied to verifying whether a sample was drawn from a population having a given probability distribution. If the distribution is binomial then the binomial test can be applied; moreover, if there are at most two samples, the Kolmogorov-Smirnov test can also be applied.

A special case of Pearson's chi-squared test is the median test, which tests the null hypothesis that the medians of two samples are equal.

Fisher's exact test is used if the variables are Bernoulli and the samples are small.

The Q test is used to discard or reject statistical data that are not in line with the sample parameters and, therefore, are possible errors.

The Shapiro-Wilk test is used to test the normality of small samples by comparing two estimators for the sample variance.

A fundamental problem in statistics is regression, i.e. the functional relationship between the measured variables extracted from a potentially infinite sample. In particular, linear regression is a method of estimating the conditional expected value of a dependent variable Y, once the values of other independent variables X (also called regressors) are known.

The case of simple linear regression is formulated as follows:

$$Y_i = \beta_0 + \beta_1 X_i + u_i$$

The beta values have already been presented as intercept and slope, plus u is the statistical error. As we have seen, it is possible to estimate these values using the least squares method.

In the case of multiple linear regression, the relationship is as follows:

$$Y_i = \beta_0 + \beta_1 X_{1i} + \beta_2 X_{2i} + \cdots + \beta_k X_{ki} + u_i$$

The method of least squares allows to find an estimate of the dependent variable which is an orthogonal projection of the vector of observations y on the space generated by the columns of the matrix describing the X independent variables.

The coefficient of determination measures the goodness of fit of the linear regression and is:

$$R^2 = \frac{\hat{\beta}' X' M_0 X \hat{\beta}}{y' M_0 y} = \frac{\hat{y}' M_0 \hat{y}}{y' M_0 y} = \frac{\sum_i (\hat{y}_i - \bar{y})^2}{\sum_i (y_i - \bar{y})^2}$$

There is also a nonlinear regression that applies to a model of the general form:

$$Y = f(X; \vartheta) + \varepsilon$$

In this case the estimation methods resort to numerical optimization algorithms or linearization processes, introducing an additional error with respect to the statistical error. From Bayes' theorem derives the Bayesian inference approach in which the probabilities are interpreted as levels of confidence for the occurrence of a given event. In Bayesian statistics, Bayes' theorem takes this form:

$$P(H_0|E) = \frac{P(E|H_0)P(H_0)}{P(E)}$$

Where E denotes the observed empirical data, while H_0 it is the null hypothesis, $P(H_0)$ it is called the prior probability, $P(E)$ it is the marginal probability, $P(H_0|E)$ it is the posterior probability, $P(E|H_0)$ it is the likelihood function. The likelihood ratio is called:

$$\Lambda = \frac{L(H_0|E)}{L(\text{not } H_0|E)} = \frac{P(E|H_0)}{P(E|\text{not } H_0)}$$

If X is distributed as a binomial random variable having a parameter distributed a priori as a beta then the same parameter distributed a posteriori also follows a beta distribution (obviously with different characteristic parameters). The same is true if X is distributed as a negative binomial random variable. If X is distributed as a gamma variable having the second parameter distributed a priori as a gamma then the same parameter distributed posteriorly also follows a gamma. The same is true if X is distributed as a Poissonian or as a normal one.

XXVIII – STOCHASTIC PROCESSES

A stochastic process represents a probabilistic dynamic system, i.e. a statistical evolution of a given system. The variables of a stochastic process are obviously random variables, they are defined on a single finite sample space and assume values in a set called state space. The characterization of a stochastic process takes place through the joint probability density function and thus it is possible to classify discrete and continuous stochastic processes.

If the transition probability between one state and the next depends on the previous states but not on time, we speak of a homogeneous stochastic process; cyclostationary stochastic processes, on the other hand, describe periodic phenomena and are particularly important in signal theory.

A Gaussian stochastic process is a stochastic process whose random variables have joint probability distribution given by a Gaussian. A Gaussian process is identified by its expected value and variance, as is a Gaussian function. In signal theory, a Gaussian process defined over time is Gaussian noise (also called white noise).

A stochastic process whose transition probability depends only on the starting state is said to be Markovian. A Markov process has the Markov property (also called no-memory):

$$\forall h > 0, t > 0 \Rightarrow \Pr[X(t+h) = y \mid X(s) = x(s), s \leq t] = \Pr[X(t+h) = y \mid X(t) = x(t)]$$

If the Markov property does not depend on time, we have homogeneous Markov processes:

$$\forall h > 0, \forall t \Rightarrow \Pr[X(t+h) = y \mid X(t) = x(t)] = \Pr[X(h) = y \mid X(0) = x(0)]$$

If a process is not Markov, it is always possible to construct Markov processes of second order, or of higher order, by taking a reference time interval of that process.

A Markov chain is a Markov process having a discrete state space. This chain can be continuous in time or discrete in time based on how the variable given by time is considered.

XXVIII – Stochastic processes

In a homogeneous Markov chain, the transition probability between states depends only on the distance of the time instants and not on the absolute value of time.

A homogeneous finite-state Markov chain is represented by a transition matrix of states and an initial probability vector. The transition matrix has all elements greater than or equal to zero (due to the properties of probabilities) and also the sum of the elements on a row is equal to one.

A discrete-state Markov chain is said to be periodic if, after a number of time steps, there is a non-zero probability of returning to the initial state of the period.

A discrete-state Markov chain is said to be irreducible if starting from each state there is a non-zero probability of reaching every other state.

A stationary probability distribution of a discrete-state homogeneous Markov chain is a discrete probability distribution that remains constant even as the Markov chain evolves over time. If the Markov chain is irreducible, such a distribution exists and is unique. If the chain is also aperiodic, the probability distribution at the nth step converges to the stationary distribution, regardless of the initial choice of the probability distribution.

Ergodic Markov chains are based on ergodic theory, itself descended from the ergodic theorem. This theorem states that a conservative transformation for the measure over a measurable space has a time mean and a space mean which coincide almost everywhere. The time average is calculated on a function that can be integrated on L^1 and the transformation thus defined is called ergodic.

In an ergodic Markov chain, the probability at any instant and for any initial condition exists and is independent of time and initial conditions.

A hidden Markov model is a Markov chain in which the states are not observable, but only the events are.

A stochastic Bernoulli process is a discrete process of independent random variables which are characterized by Bernoulli's law. Also in this process there is a lack of memory.

Given, for each random variable, the probability of success p (and that of failure given by 1-p), the number of successes after n trials follows the binomial law B(p,n), while the number of trials to obtain a success follows the geometric law of ratio equal to 1-p.

A stochastic Poisson process is a process that generalizes the Bernoulli process to the continuum. It is also an example of a continuous-time Markov chain. The increments are stationary, i.e. they depend only on the length of the time interval considered and have a Poisson distribution equal to:

$$\forall k \in N \Rightarrow P(N_{t+\tau} - N_t = k) = \frac{e^{-\lambda\tau}(\lambda\tau)^k}{k!}$$

At the nth time, the event follows the gamma distribution with parameters given by n and the inverse of the intensity. If only one event has occurred in a certain time interval, then the Poisson process has a uniform distribution. Given two independent Poisson processes, their sum is still a Poisson process given by the sum of the intensities of the individual processes.

A compound Poisson process is a continuous time process on the set of natural numbers whose "jumps" between one number and another are defined by a law related to a Poisson process. In particular we have, for any t>0:

$$Y(t) = \sum_{i=1}^{N(t)} D_i$$

Where N(t) is a Poisson process and D are the independent random variables defined on the set of natural numbers. The expected value and the variance are defined as follows:

$$E(Y(t)) = \lambda t E(D)$$
$$Var(Y(t)) = \lambda t E(D^2)$$

A Lévy process is a continuous stochastic process with stationary and independent increments. At time zero, the process is almost certainly null. A Poisson process is a particular Lévy process.

A Markov chain whose transitions are given by random variables is called a random walk. This process can be seen as a discretization of a Lévy process.

In the one-dimensional random walk, the random variable that provides the number of steps in one direction after N movements is a discrete variable with a binomial distribution. The probability of returning to the origin tends to the certain event for a number of movements which tends to infinity.

XXVIII – Stochastic processes

For the two-dimensional case, two stochastically independent binomial random variables are defined, while for the three-dimensional case the variables become three.

The transition to the continuum of a random walk leads to a Lévy process whose increments are given by random variables. This process is a model for Brownian motion which is an important result of statistical physics applied to classical mechanics.

A Wiener process is a Lévy process, which is also Gaussian, used to model Brownian motion. The time intervals of such a process are represented by a Gaussian distribution of mean date and variance. It is also possible to define a Wiener measure, that is a probability law induced by the Wiener process on the space of continuous functions and associate an integral, called Wiener's, to this measure.

Furthermore, the differential of a Wiener process can also be defined as that process which has the mean quadratic coincident with the differential of the quadratic mean of the starting Wiener process:

$$E(dW_t^2) = dE(W_t^2)$$

Having defined the differential of the process in this way:

$$dW_t = N\sqrt{dt}$$

XXIX – NUMERICAL ANALYSIS

Numerical analysis is a complementary sector of mathematics to what has been said in almost all of this manual and also in relation to the concepts of elementary mathematics. The importance of this analysis affects aspects of algebra, matrix mathematics, mathematical analysis, differential equations and many mathematical problems. The advent of computers has then given a great boost to this sector, above all for the immense computing power available and the consequent results, which now span every application field. We will not repeat what has already been said in *the "Elementary Mathematics Manual"* about numerical calculus applied to matrices and polynomials: those notions are the basis of any numerical analysis.

A first class of numerical methods is that relating to the interpolation and extrapolation of functions, following a discretization procedure which characterizes the transition from the continuum of mathematical analysis to the discrete of numerical analysis.
The linear extrapolation of a given point, with respect to its neighbors, is given by the following relationship:

$$y(x_*) = y_{k-1} + \frac{x_* - x_{k-1}}{x_k - x_{k-1}}(y_k - y_{k-1})$$

This extrapolation is essential for applications of linear regression.
A basic idea of polynomial interpolation is to express any function as an approximation of high order polynomials. However, this idea is contraindicated on the basis of Runge's phenomenon, which demonstrates how, in some cases, the linear interpolation error tends to infinity.
A first method to reduce this error, as the degree of polynomial increases, is to use the Cebichev nodes instead of equidistant points for the interpolation. These nodes are defined as follows:

$$x_i := \cos\left(\frac{2i - 1}{2n}\pi\right)$$

Where n is the degree of the polynomial and ei is an integer between 1 and n. These points are the roots of the Cebichev polynomials:

$$T_n = \cos(n\vartheta)$$

These polynomials are the solutions of the Cebichev differential equation:

$$(1 - x^2)\, y'' - x\, y' + n^2\, y = 0$$

Another way to reduce the polynomial interpolation error is to use spline functions. These functions consist of sets of polynomials connected to each other so that, in a given interval, they are continuous with continuous derivatives, at least up to a certain order of derivation. The connection points between polynomials are called spline nodes, and polynomial interpolation with spline functions is called spline interpolation. Through this mechanism, Runge's phenomenon does not occur.

We give below some definitions that will be useful throughout the numerical analysis.

Numerical stability is a property which guarantees the limitation of the error, but at the same time the non-cancellation of the error itself. In other words, a numerical algorithm will be stable if its approximation error with respect to the real case is a finite number or an infinitesimal, but not zero.

If this error becomes zero, the phenomenon of numerical cancellation occurs.

Conditioning is a measure of the ratio of error to data uncertainty. A problem is well conditioned when the solution, under small perturbations, does not vary much from the solution to the original problem. Conversely, the problem is ill-conditioned. Examples of conditioning numerical problems are given by the numerical calculation of the roots of a polynomial or by the numerical solution of systems of equations or matrices. There are several ways to measure the conditioning of a numerical problem, for example in fluid dynamics the Peclet number is used, even if generally a good conditioning number is the spectral one, related to the two norm, calculated as the ratio between the spectral radius and the minimum of the solving eigenvalues. This ratio is always greater than one, as it grows we have a measure of the bad conditioning of the problem.

Connected to the problem of numerical cancellation and conditioning is the concept of inherent error, i.e. the error that is committed by representing a real number, in particular irrational numbers or periodic rational numbers, with a finite number of digits, as happens in all practical cases, from calculators to manual calculation.

Assuming that the error on the initial data is given by:

$$\varepsilon_x = \frac{(x_p - x_r)}{x_r}$$

The inherent error can be expressed as:

$$\varepsilon_y = \frac{|f(x_p) - f(x_r)|}{|f(x_r)|}$$

If it is much greater than the initial error, then the problem is ill-conditioned.

Another major area of numerical analysis is that of discretizing the operations of mathematical analysis.

Numerical integration consists in calculating a definite integral without analytically calculating the primitive. There are many numerical methods for calculating the numerical integral.

Newton-Cotes formulas assume that the value of the function to be integrated is known in a series of equidistant points. The closed form of these formulas also considers the ends of the integration interval, the open one does not.

For the closed form there is this relationship:

$$\int_a^b f(x)\, dx \approx \sum_{i=0}^{n} w_i\, f(x_i)$$

Each point is spaced by a quantity called pitch, while the multiplicative coefficients are called weights and come from Lagrange polynomials. The open form can be expressed as follows:

XXIX – Numerical analysis

$$\int_a^b f(x)\,dx \approx \sum_{i=1}^{n-1} w_i\, f(x_i)$$

The trapezium rule is a closed Newton-Cotes formula which considers a pitch equal to:

$$\frac{h}{2}(f_0 + f_1)$$

and has an error given by:

$$-\frac{h^3}{12} f^{(2)}(\xi)$$

This rule can be expressed as follows:

$$\int_a^b f(x)\,dx \approx (b-a)\frac{f(a)+f(b)}{2}$$

Another rule that can be derived from the closed Newton-Cotes formulas is the Cavalieri-Simpson rule, also known as the method of parabolas. The step and the error are defined as follows:

$$\frac{h}{3}(f_0 + 4f_1 + f_2)$$

$$-\frac{h^5}{90} f^{(4)}(\xi)$$

As you can see, this rule is more precise than that of the trapezoid. The rule is therefore:

$$\int_a^b f(x)\,dx \simeq \frac{h}{3}[(y_0 + 4y_1 + y_2) + (y_2 + 4y_3 + y_4) + \ldots + (y_{n-2} + 4y_{n-1} + y_n)]$$

XXIX – Numerical analysis

There are other more precise rules that can be obtained from closed Newton-Cotes formulas such as Boole's rule.

From the open Newton-Cotes formulas we obtain the rectangle rule, also known as the midpoint rule, which has pitch and error given by:

$$2h f_1$$

$$\frac{h^3}{24} f^{(2)}(\xi)$$

This rule can be expressed as:

$$\int_a^b f(x)dx \approx (b-a)f\left(\frac{a+b}{2}\right)$$

As for the closed Newton-Cotes formulas, also for the open ones there are other rules that reduce the error, such as Masina's rule. Furthermore, the rectangle rule can be composed with other rules.

The major problem of the Newton-Cotes formulas lies in the fact that, for many large n, one can observe Runge's phenomenon. Therefore, other more stable methods of numerical integration are needed, among these there is the quadrature of Gauss.

This method considers n+1 nodal points in the integration interval that are the zeros of an orthogonal polynomial with respect to a weight function and interpolates the integral with this formula:

$$\int_a^b f(x)w(x)dx = \sum_{i=0}^n f(x_i)w_i$$

As in the case of the Newton-Cotes formulas, the weight functions can be expressed on the basis of the coefficients of the Lagrange polynomials:

$$\int_a^b l_i(x)w(x)dx$$

XXIX – Numerical analysis

The calculation of integrals of functions of several variables uses advanced methods, among which the Monte Carlo numerical methods. The numerical approximation of the derivative passes from the concept of finite difference. It can be expressed like this:

$$\Delta_{c,h} f(x) = f(x + c + \frac{h}{2}) - f(x + c - \frac{h}{2}) \quad \forall c, h \in \mathbb{R}$$

Where c is the center eh is the pitch of the difference. There are three types of finite difference, the centered one, the forward one and the backward one, defined as follows:

$$\Delta_0 f(x) = \Delta_{0,h} f(x) = f(x + \frac{h}{2}, h) - f(x - \frac{h}{2})$$

$$\Delta_h f(x) = \Delta_{\frac{h}{2},h} f(x) = f(x + h) - f(x)$$

$$\Delta_{-h} f(x) = \Delta_{-\frac{h}{2},h} f(x) = f(x) - f(x - h)$$

It is also possible to define operators to the differences which exploit the previous definitions, which are linear and respond to the Leibnitz rule. For example, the forward difference operator is given by:

$$\Delta_h = T_h - I$$

$$T_h(f) = f(x + h)$$

Where I is the identity. The n-th order finite differences are expressed as follows:

$$\Delta_h^n f(x) = \sum_{i=0}^{n} (-1)^i \binom{n}{i} f(x + (n - i)h)$$

$$\Delta_{-h}^n f(x) = \sum_{i=0}^{n} (-1)^i \binom{n}{i} f(x - ih)$$

$$\Delta_0^n f(x) = \sum_{i=0}^{n} (-1)^i \binom{n}{i} f\left(x + \left(\frac{n}{2} - i\right) h\right)$$

Finite differences are fundamental for numerically approximating a derivative. Thus we have centered forward and backward numerical derivatives. For example, for the first derivative we have:

$$f'(x_i) \approx \frac{f(x_{i+1}) - f(x_{i-1})}{2h}$$

$$f'(x_i) \approx \frac{f(x_{i+1}) - f(x_i)}{h}$$

$$f'(x_i) \approx \frac{f(x_i) - f(x_{i-1})}{h}$$

The substitution of the analytic derivatives with finite differences gives rise to the method of finite differences which is the main numerical method for solving ordinary differential equations. This method causes an ordinary differential equation to become a difference equation that can be solved both in numerical terms and using discrete analytical tools, such as the zeta transform. Difference methods are defined as one-step if the n+1-th value depends only on the n-th value, otherwise it is called multi-step.

The one-step difference method that exploits the forward finite differences is called explicit Euler method, the one that exploits the backward finite differences is called implicit Euler method, whose generic solution formula is given by:

$$y_{n+1} = y_n + hf(x_{n+1}, y_{n+1})$$

Other one-step methods are the trapezium method, also called Crank-Nicholson:

$$y_{n+1} = y_n + \frac{h}{2}(f_n + f_{n+1}) = y_n + \frac{h}{2}(y_n' + y_{n+1}')$$

XXIX – Numerical analysis

Heun's:

$$y_{n+1} = y_n + \frac{h}{2}(f(x_n, y_n) + f(x_n + h, y_{n+1}^{(0)}))$$

$$y_{n+1}^{(0)} = y_n + hf_n$$

And the Euler exponential:

$$y_{n+1} = e^{-Bh}y_n + B^{-1}(1 - e^{-Bh})A$$

Which holds if the differential equation is of the form:

$$y'(t) = A - By(t)$$

Multistep methods are given by the Adams-Bashforth one:

$$y_{n+1} = y_n + \frac{h}{12}(23f_n - 16f_{n-1} + 5f_{n-2})$$

And from that of Adams-Moulton:

$$y_{n+1} = y_n + \frac{h}{12}(5f_{n+1} + 8f_n - f_{n-1})$$

The Runge-Kutta methods are instead a family of one-step numerical iterative methods for solving ordinary differential equations, in particular for Cauchy problems. The definition interval of the Cauchy problem is divided evenly according to the following step:

$$h = \frac{t_f - t_0}{n}$$

These methods state that the numerical resolution of a Cauchy problem is given by:

$$\begin{cases} y_{n+1} = y_n + h \sum_{i=1}^{s} b_i f(t_n + \theta_i h, Y_i) \\ Y_i = y_n + h \sum_{j=1}^{s} a_{ij} f(t_n + \theta_j h, Y_j) \quad i = 1, \ldots, s \end{cases}$$

Where in the summations there are the quadrature formulas on the nodes that contain the respective weights, as already explained previously for other numerical methods.

Furthermore, there are numerical methods for solving differential equations which exploit the numerical approximations of power series. Numerical methods are said to be convergent if the numerical solution approximates the exact solution for a step tending to zero:

$$\lim_{h \to 0+} \max_{n=0,1,\ldots,\lfloor t^* /h \rfloor} \| y_{n,h} - y(t_n) \| = 0.$$

While they are said to be consistent if the truncation error tends to zero for a step that tends to zero:

$$\lim_{h \to 0} \frac{\delta_{n+k}^h}{h} = 0.$$

Finally the order p of a numerical method is defined as follows (for a step tending to zero):

$$\delta_{n+k}^h = O(h^{p+1})$$

A method for the numerical solution of partial differential equations is given by the finite volume method. Basically it is a question of dividing the integration domain into a finite number of volumes and of integrating the equations in these volumes with boundary conditions defined on the boundaries of each single volume. This method represents a simplification of a much more widespread method which is that of finite elements.

The first phase of this method consists in modeling the mathematical problem using a differential equation, generally with partial derivatives. The modeling starts from the assumption that the real case neglects some parameters considered non-fundamental while focusing on others, obviously depending on the boundary conditions. The second phase passes through the discretization of the finite element model both in space and in time to bring the system from an infinite number of degrees of freedom to a finite number, all to be processed numerically. In this discretization phase, other errors are generated which must not affect either the stability or the consistency of the solutions found on the basis of this method.

A finite element is distinguished by its dimension (one, two or three dimensional), by the nodes which are precise points which identify its geometry, by the degrees of freedom (the values which the functions and their gradients in the nodes can assume) and by the forces on the nodes, which take into account the support reactions and the boundary conditions on the nodes.

The fundamental procedure that distinguishes finite elements from other numerical methods is the mapping of the space, also called mesh, which is never a uniform mapping, but which uses calculation algorithms to adapt to the individual models examined from time to time. Therefore, the finite elements are almost never evenly distributed.

In many cases it is necessary to introduce pre-conditioning of the model to guarantee the stability of the solution and this is done using matrix methods of elementary numerical analysis, for example the pre-conditioning matrices, also called stiffness matrices.

The finite element method is based on the Galerkin scheme, i.e. on the weak formulation of partial differential equations. Therefore, to guarantee the existence and uniqueness of the solution, the Lax-Milgram lemma becomes fundamental which requires that, in this equation, the form a(u,v) is bilinear and coercive:

$$a\left(u, v\right) = l\left(v\right), \forall v \in V$$

Where V is a generic Hilbert space. Galerkin's method decomposes the discretization of this problem into finding a solution in a sequence of subspaces such that we have:

$$\{V_n\}_{n=1}^{+\infty} \subset V$$

$$\bigcup_{n=1}^{+\infty} V_n = V$$

In each of these finite-dimensional subspaces the initial problem can be solved exactly from the discrete point of view. We therefore have that the general problem on infinite-dimensional spaces reduces to finding n solutions of discrete problems on finite-dimensional spaces in this way:

$$a\left(u_n, v\right) = l\left(v\right), \forall v \in V_n$$

At this point it is enough to remember that every solution can be expressed as a linear combination of a basis of the subspace:

$$u_n = \sum_{j=1}^{N_n} U_j v_j$$

By defining three matrices that respectively condense the solutions, the boundary conditions and the coefficients:

$$\mathbf{K_n} = \left\{s_{ij}\right\}_{i,j=1}^{N_n}, s_{ij} = a\left(v_j, v_i\right)$$

$$\mathbf{F_n} = \left\{f_i\right\}_{i=1}^{N_n}, f_i = l\left(v_i\right)$$

$$\mathbf{X_n} = \left\{U_i\right\}_{i=1}^{N_n}$$

Galerkin's method defines the following system of linear algebraic equations in matrix form:

$$\mathbf{K_n} \cdot \mathbf{X_n} = \mathbf{F}_n$$

Which can be solved with the usual classical numerical methods. It can be shown that for elliptic equations the Galerkin method converges:

$$\lim_{n \to +\infty} \|u - u_n\|_V = 0$$

Furthermore, by Cea's lemma, Galerkin's method is strongly consistent, i.e.:

$$\forall v_h \in V_h : a(u - u_h, v_h) = 0$$

XXIX – Numerical analysis

For hyperbolic equations it is necessary to refer to the forward Euler scheme, also called upwind to the backward Euler scheme or to higher order schemes such as those of Lax-Friedrichs and Lax-Wendroff. For example for a one-dimensional wave equation:

$$\frac{\partial u}{\partial t} + a\frac{\partial u}{\partial x} = 0$$

The discretization according to the forward Euler scheme is convergent if this condition holds:

$$c = \left|\frac{a\Delta t}{\Delta x}\right| \leq 1.$$

This is called the Courant-Friedrichs-Lewy (CFL) condition. As can be seen, this condition imposes a limit on the relationship between temporal and spatial discretization. The parameter a usually has size and speed meaning. At the n-dimensional level the condition transforms like this:

$$C = \Delta t \sum_{i=1}^{n} \frac{u_{x_i}}{\Delta x_i} \leq C_{max}.$$

However, this condition is only necessary and not sufficient for convergence. As far as the search for sufficient conditions for the convergence of hyperbolic equations is concerned, even more stringent conditions are needed, such as limitations on the diffusion coefficients, also known as numerical diffusion (an example is the limitation of the Peclet number for fluid-dynamic hyperbolic equations).

Also for partial differential equations, the leapfrog scheme can be used which, unlike the forward Euler scheme, is a second-order method that can be used for equations of the form:

$$\ddot{x} = F(x)$$

And the discretizations are given by:

$$x_i = x_{i-1} + v_{i-1/2}\,\Delta t,$$

$$a_i = F(x_i)$$

$$v_{i+1/2} = v_{i-1/2} + a_i\,\Delta t,$$

In this scheme the time discretization must be constant to maintain the convergence of the solution.

A further category of numerical methods is related to the discretization of transforms, in particular the Fourier one which gives rise to the fast Fourier transform algorithm.

XXIX – Numerical analysis

XXX – FRACTAL GEOMETRY

Fractal geometry deals with objects, called fractals, with internal homothety. This property is called self-similarity and guarantees that, on whatever scale the fractal is observed, the object always has the same global characteristics. A fractal is not constructed with a function described in suitable coordinates, but with an algorithm, typically recursive. Based on the equation that defines the algorithm, linear, non-linear or random fractals can be defined.

The Hausdorff dimension of a metric space is the number of balls of maximum radius r needed to completely cover the metric space. This dimension is the threshold value below which the Hausdorff measure in those dimensions is infinite and above which the measure is zero. For any subset B of the metric space X, the Hausdorff dimension defined on a ball A is as follows:

$$H_\delta^s(B) = \inf\left\{\sum_{i=1}^{\infty} diam(A_i)^s\right\}$$

The exterior Hausdorff dimension of the metric space is:

$$H^s(B) = \lim_{\delta \to 0} H_\delta^s(B)$$

The following equality holds only if B and C are disjoint and Borel sets:

$$H^s(B \cup C) = H^s(B) + H^s(C)$$

All Borel subsets of the metric space are measurable, and the exterior Hausdorff dimension is a countable, additive measure.

The Hausdorff dimension of an n-dimensional Euclidean space R is just n, that of the circle of unit radius is one, while countable sets have Hausdorff dimension zero.

Given a topological space, the topological dimension is the smallest integer n for which every open cover has a refinement in which every point is contained in at most n+1 sets. An n-dimensional Euclidean

XXX – Fractal geometry

space R has topological dimension n, a graph having a finite number of vertices and edges has topological dimension one.

For fractals the Hausdorff dimension is always greater than the topological dimension.

The Minkowski-Boulingand dimension determines the dimension of a set S in a metric space. Given N(x) the number of cells of lateral length x needed to cover the set, then the Minkowski-Boulingand dimension is defined as follows:

$$\dim_{MB}(A) = \lim_{x \to 0} \frac{\log N(x)}{\log\left(\frac{1}{x}\right)}$$

If such limit does not exist, then we speak of upper and lower dimension which correspond to the upper and lower bound of the expression. The Minkowski-Boulingand dimension is always greater than or equal to the Hausdorff dimension. These two dimensions are the most common fractal dimensions.

The Mandelbrot set is a fractal that is a subset of the complex plane, defined as follows:

$$M = \left\{ c \in C : \sup_{n \in N} \left| f_c^n(0) \right| < \infty \right\}$$
$$f_c(z) = z^2 + c$$

If the modulus of the generic complex number is greater than 2, the sequence diverges and therefore the point is outside the Mandelbrot set. Given a holomorphic function in complex analysis, a Julia set is a set of all points whose behavior is chaotic after repeated iterations. The Julia set is connected if the point belongs to the Mandelbrot set.

If the complex function is defined like this:

$$f_c(z) = \left(\left| \mathrm{Re}(z) \right| + i \left| \mathrm{Im}(z) \right| \right)^2 + c$$

Then a new fractal arises, called a burning ship.

The Cantor set is a subset of the real interval [0,1] obtained recursively by removing a central open segment at each step: for example, in the first step the open sub-interval between 1/3 and 2 is eliminated /3. The

268

Cantor set has zero Lebesgue measure and, at the same time, it is an uncountable set, endowed with the cardinality of the continuum. Furthermore it is a closed subset of the interval [0,1], it is compact, each of its points is of accumulation, its internal part is empty and it is a totally disconnected set.

The Cantor set is a fractal whose Hausdorff dimension is as follows:

$$H^s = \frac{\ln 2}{\ln 3}$$

The Cantor dust is a multi-dimensional version of the Cantor set obtained by multiplying the Cantor set with itself a finite number of times at the level of the Cartesian product. The Cantor dust is a particular Cantor space, ie a topological space homeomorphic to the Cantor set. A Cantor space is generated by a topological product of a countable number of Cantor sets.

Given a topological space, it is Cantor space if and only it is non-empty, each of its points is of accumulation, it is compact, it is totally disconnected, it is metrizable and it has the cardinality of the continuum.

The Cantor function is a function that generalizes the Cantor set to the functional scope. This function is continuous and increasing, but has zero derivative almost everywhere, as it is constant in all sub-intervals of [0,1].

The Koch curve is a fractal curve which is constructed with a recursive algorithm very similar to the one used for the Cantor set. Each segment is divided into three equal parts, the central segment is canceled and replaced with two identical segments which become two sides of an equilateral triangle, then the same mechanism is carried out for all the segments. This curve is continuous, has infinite length, is self-similar (as a fractal) and cannot be derived at any point.

A particular Koch curve is the Peano curve, ie a curve, parametrized by a continuous function that completely covers a square starting from the interval [0,1]. This function is therefore surjective and it can be seen how it coincides with the Cantor function: the consequence of this is that the Peano curve is not injective nor differentiable.

Other fractal curves are the Sierpinski curves which are a sequence of n continuous closed plane curves. As n tends to infinity, these curves fill the unit square and hence the Hausdorff dimension is two. The Euclidean length is equal to:

$$l_n = \frac{2(1+\sqrt{2})}{3}2^n - \frac{2-\sqrt{2}}{3\cdot 2^n}$$

The Sierpinski carpet is a fractal that is obtained by starting from a square, dividing it into nine smaller equal squares, removing the central square and iterating the algorithm for all the existing squares. This fractal is a closed, limited and compact whole, it has the cardinality of the continuum and a zero Lebesgue measure. Furthermore, it has topological dimension equal to one and is a universal planar curve. The Hausdorff dimension is as follows:

$$H^s = \frac{\log 8}{\log 3}$$

If instead of the square we have a triangle divided into four equal and smaller triangles we obtain the Sierpinski triangle which has Hausdorff dimension:

$$H^s = \frac{\log 3}{\log 2}$$

A three-dimensional version of the Sierpinski carpet is the fractal called Menger sponge. In this case we start from a cube and divide it into 27 equal sub-cubes, always eliminating the central one. Each of the six faces of Menger's sponge is a Sierpinski carpet. The topological dimension of the Menger sponge is equal to one, the Hausdorff one is as follows:

$$H^s = \frac{\log 20}{\log 3}$$

All the fractals presented so far are deterministic. The random fractals are, for example, the random walk and the Brownian motion (which has a Hausdorff dimension equal to two).
For all fractals it is possible to draw up a list based on the increasing value of the Hausdorff dimension. The complete calculation of fractals is possible only thanks to the computing power of computers while

their use is extended to scientific disciplines such as statistics, physics and chemistry.

XXX – Fractal geometry

XXXI – NUMBER THEORY

Number theory deals mainly with pure mathematics problems related to integers. At a basic level, number theory problems concern the concepts of divisibility, Euclid's algorithm for the greatest common divisor and least common multiple. At an advanced level, number theory searches for the relationships between the various types of prime numbers, sequences of integers and some particular functions, such as those of Euler, establishing numerous conjectures.

A natural number is said to be perfect when it is equal to the sum of its proper divisors, defective when it is greater than the sum of its proper divisors, and abundant when it is less than this sum. All prime numbers and their powers are defective numbers as are all proper divisors of defective numbers and perfect numbers. All integer multiples of abundant numbers and perfect numbers are abundant numbers.

A natural number is said to be slightly defective if the sum of its proper divisors is equal to the number minus one and is said to be slightly abundant if this sum is equal to the number plus one. All powers of two are slightly defective numbers.

A natural number is said to be semi-perfect if it is equal to the sum of some of its divisors. A semi-perfect number cannot be defective, but it can be abundant.

One can construct an arithmetic of the integers with a congruence relation called module n: this arithmetic takes the name of modular. Given three integers a, b, n with n different from zero, then a and b are congruent modulo n if their difference is a multiple of n and it is written like this:

$$a \equiv b \ (\mathrm{mod}\, n)$$

This congruence is an equivalence relation, holding the reflexive, symmetric and transitive properties. Furthermore, congruence is invariant under addition, multiplication and exponentiation and therefore the commutative, associative and distributive properties are also valid. However, the product of two non-zero elements can give a null result provided that n is not a prime number. This congruence relation forms a finite cyclic group, therefore abelian; with the operations of sum and product, it forms a ring.

273

XXXI – Theory of numbers

Fermat's little theorem states that given a prime number p, for every integer a the following relation holds:

$$a^p \equiv a \ (\mathrm{mod} \ p)$$

This means that, if p is prime and a is a coprime number ap, then:

$$a^{p-1} \equiv 1 \ (\mathrm{mod} \ p)$$

We define the φ Euler function, also called the totient function, as the number of integers between 1 and n that are coprime to n. The totient function of the product is equal to the product of the totient functions, furthermore if p is a prime number and k>0 we have that:

$$\varphi(p^k) = (p-1)p^{k-1} \Leftrightarrow \varphi(p) = p-1$$

For n greater than or equal to three, the Euler function is even. A number for which the following equation has no solution is said to be nontient:

$$\varphi(x) = n$$

All prime numbers except one are non-living. A number for which the following relation holds is called cocotient:

$$x - \varphi(x) = n$$

If there are no solutions, the number is said to be non-cotient.
Euler's theorem states that, if n is a positive integer and a is coprime with respect to n, then the following relation holds:

$$a^{\varphi(n)} \equiv 1 \ (\mathrm{mod} \ n)$$

This theorem is a generalization of Fermat's little theorem.
A Fermat number is an integer that can be expressed in this form:

$$n \in N \Rightarrow F_n = 2^{2^n} + 1$$

A prime number such that the previous relation also holds is called a Fermat prime. In a binary number system, all Fermat numbers are palindromes and all Fermat primes are palindrome primes. Since there are infinitely many Fermat numbers and every prime number divides at most one Fermat number, it remains proven that the prime numbers are infinite. Furthermore, no Fermat number can be expressed as the sum of two prime numbers, and the sum of the reciprocals of all Fermat numbers is irrational.

Fermat's primality test is derived from Fermat's little theorem. If there exists a number a such that Fermat's little theorem does not hold for a given n, then n is not prime.

We can define a pseudoprime as a number that behaves like a prime number, even if it is not prime. In particular, a number that respects Fermat's little theorem and Fermat's primality test, even if it is not a prime number, is called Fermat's pseudoprime. A pseudoprime Fermat number with respect to every a coprime is called a Carmichael number.

A positive integer is a Carmichael number if and only if it is square-free and, for any prime divisor p of n, (p-1) divides (n-1). From this it follows that all Carmichael numbers are odd, furthermore all Carmichael numbers satisfy Fermat's test of primality.

We can define the Carmichael function as:

$$\lambda(n) = mcm\left(\left\{\varphi(p_i^i)\right\}\right)$$

Where the different p take into account the factorization into prime numbers. Carmichael's theorem states that, given integer coprime with n, then the Carmichael function of n is the smallest positive integer m such that the following relation holds:

$$a^m \equiv 1 \;(\mathrm{mod}\,n)$$

This theorem generalizes Euler's one.

A number is called Euler pseudoprime based on if it is a composite odd number and is:

$$a^{\frac{n-1}{2}} \equiv \pm 1 \;(\mathrm{mod}\,n)$$

Every Euler pseudoprime is also a Fermat pseudoprime. Euler pseudoprime numbers which are coprime in any base are called absolute Euler pseudoprimes and are a subset of the Carmichael numbers.

Given a prime number p and an integer a, the Legendre symbol is defined as follows:

$$\left(\frac{a}{p}\right) = \begin{cases} 0 \Leftrightarrow \dfrac{a}{p} = n \in N \\ 1 \Leftrightarrow \exists k \in N : k^2 \equiv a(\bmod\, p) \\ -1 \Leftrightarrow \exists k \in N : k^2 \neq a(\bmod\, p) \end{cases}$$

If p is any integer, the Legendre symbol is generalized from the Jacobi symbol. Legendre's symbol is a fully multiplicative function, furthermore the quadratic reciprocity law (or Gauss's golden theorem) holds:

$$\left(\frac{q}{p}\right) = \left(\frac{p}{q}\right)(-1)^{\left(\frac{p-1}{2}\right)\left(\frac{q-1}{2}\right)}$$

A number is called Euler-Jacobi pseudoprime if this relation holds:

$$a^{\frac{n-1}{2}} \equiv \left(\frac{a}{n}\right)(\bmod\, n)$$

All Euler-Jacobi pseudoprimes are Euler pseudoprimes.

A number is said to be Mersenne if it can be expressed as follows:

$$M_n = 2^n - 1$$

Where n is a prime positive integer. If the Mersenne number is prime, we have a Mersenne prime. All perfect numbers can be expressed in Mersenne numbers as follows:

$$\frac{M_n(M_n+1)}{2} = 2^{n-1}(2^n-1)$$

Related to the Mersenne numbers is the Lucas-Lehmer primality test. We define a recursive sequence like this:

$$L_1 = 4$$
$$L_{n+1} = L_n^2 - 2$$

The Lucas-Lehmer primality test states that, given a prime integer, the corresponding Mersenne number is prime if and only if:

$$L_{n-1} \equiv 0 \pmod{M_n}$$

Wilson's theorem states that a natural number greater than one is a prime number if and only if the following relation holds:

$$(n-1)! \equiv -1 \pmod{n}$$

Wilson's primality test derives from this theorem, which however is not applicable in computational problems given the intervention of the factorial operation, which is particularly onerous due to the complexity of the algorithm.

A result of modular arithmetic is the so-called Chinese remainder theorem. Given k pairwise coprime integers, then however we choose a basis of other k integers, there exists an integer solution of the following system of congruences:

$$\forall i = 1,...,k \mid x \equiv a_i \pmod{n_i}$$

All the solutions of this system are congruent in modulus to the product of the n k-ths. We can generalize this theorem to algebraic structures such as groups and rings.

The Mobius function is equal to -1 if the positive integer can be decomposed into an odd number of distinct prime factors, it is equal to 0 if there are one or more repeating prime factors and it is +1 if the number can be decomposed into an even number of distinct prime factors. This function is multiplicative if the integers are coprime and

the sum of all the values of the function on all the divisors of an integer
is equal to zero, except for n=1 in which the sum is equal to one.
The Mertens function associates to each positive integer n, an integer
obtained as the sum of the values of the Mobius function between 1 and
n. It can be written like this:

$$M(n) = \sum_{k=1}^{n} \mu(k)$$

Where in the summation there is the Mobius function. For the Mertens
function the following relation holds:

$$|M(n)| \le n$$

For every real number, defined as a function that is equal to the number
of primes less than or equal to the number, the prime number theorem
states that this function tends asymptotically to the ratio between the
number and its natural logarithm:

$$\pi(x) \propto \frac{x}{\ln x}$$

A famous number theory theorem recently proved (1994) is Fermat's
Last Theorem. It states that there are no positive integer solutions, for
n>2, to the following equation:

$$a^n + b^n = c^n$$

The theory of numbers has a particular sector, called analytic theory of
numbers, in which the methods of mathematical analysis are used to
apply them to the theory of numbers. An example has just been given
via the prime number theorem, while another is given by the Riemann
Hypothesis.
This hypothesis constitutes Hilbert's problem 8 (being part of the
famous 24 Hilbert problems posed at the beginning of the twentieth
century). The hypothesis is a conjecture on the distribution of nontrivial zeros of the Riemann zeta function defined on a complex number
with real part greater than one and analytically extendable by means of
meromorphic functions.

XXXI – Theory of numbers

The Riemann Hypothesis states that the real part of any nontrivial root is ½. It has not yet been demonstrated, however it is considered a conjecture because it is believed to be true.

There is a link between this hypothesis and the prime numbers, given that for every real number greater than one the Euler product formula calculated on the prime numbers is valid therefore the distribution of the zeros of the zeta function is linked to the distribution of the prime numbers in the set of numbers natural.

Another result is given by Matiyasevich's theorem which answers Hilbert's tenth problem in the negative: it is not possible to construct a general algorithm to establish whether a system of Diophantine equations has integer solutions. This theorem states that every recursively countable set is Diophantine.

Another unsolved conjecture is that of Collatz: given a positive integer, if it is one the algorithm terminates, if it is even it is divided by two, otherwise it is multiplied by three and one is added. The conjecture states that this algorithm always fails, regardless of the starting value. One can formulate this conjecture in terms of algebraic structures and combinatorial geometry.

The Wagstaff number is defined as a prime number of the form:

$$p = \frac{2^q + 1}{3}$$

With q prime number. Mersenne's new conjecture states that for any odd natural number, if at least two of the following statements are true, then the third is also true. The three statements are: p is a Mersenne prime, p is a Wagstaff prime, p is expressed in these two alternative ways, for some natural k:

$$p = 2^k \pm 1$$
$$p = 4^k \pm 3$$

This conjecture is also not yet proven. However, the classical Mersenne conjecture is not true.

We call twin primes two prime numbers that differ from each other by two. They are called cousins, primes that differ by four and sexy primes that differ by six.

XXXI – Theory of numbers

A Sophie Germain prime is a prime p such that 2p+1 is also prime (the latter number is called a sure prime). Sophie Germain's primes are related to Mersenne's primes and Fermat's last theorem.

The twin prime conjecture states that there are infinitely many prime numbers p such that p+2 is prime. Polignac's conjecture generalizes this result by stating that, for any natural number k, there are infinitely many pairs of primes that differ by 2k. These conjectures are unproven.

The Hardy-Littlewood conjecture concerns the distribution of twin prime numbers and is an analogue of the prime number theorem.

Another famous unproven conjecture is Goldbach's conjecture in both its strong and weak forms. The first states that every even number greater than two can be written as the sum of two prime numbers, while the second formulates the same problem by saying that every odd number greater than seven can be expressed as the sum of three odd prime numbers.

The strong conjecture implies the weak one, moreover there are modern results that indicate that the generalized Riemann hypothesis implies the Goldbach conjecture, while lately there have been significant steps towards the possible proof of the conjecture in weak form.

XXXII – ADVANCED MATHEMATICAL LOGIC

Advanced mathematical logic takes its cue from the elementary foundations already described at the beginning of the *"Elementary Mathematics Manual"* and draws fundamental consequences for the development of all the previously exposed mathematical sectors.

The theory of orders studies some binary relationships that induce an ordering of the elements. A binary relation is called order if the reflexive, antisymmetric and transitive properties hold and the set in which this relation holds is called ordered. A binary relation that satisfies only the reflexive and transitive properties is called a preorder. If instead of the reflexive property, there is the anti-reflexive one, then we speak of strict order or preorder. If the order or preorder relation is satisfied for all elements of the set, then we speak of total order or preorder. Through an equivalence relation and the use of the quotient set, it is always possible to construct an order starting from a preorder.

Within an order we call minimum (or maximum) the smallest (or largest) value assumed in the reference set. If these values are unique, we speak of a minimum and a maximum. The maximum (minimum) value in that subset is called the major (or minor) of a subset. The upper bound is the minimum of the set of majorants, the lower bound is the maximum of the set of minorants. A subset with a major and a minor is called bounded. It can be seen that the minimum and the maximum may not exist, but there could be multiple minimal or maximal elements, furthermore the same element can be minimal and maximal.

In order theory, the logical principle of duality holds, i.e. if a given proposition is true for every partially ordered set, then its dual proposition is still true for every partially ordered set. The proposition obtained by exchanging every inequality and inverting every term with its symmetric is called dual.

A monotonic function is an order-preserving function, so if $x<y$ then also $f(x)<f(y)$ and if the converse is also true, the function is an order embedding. A surjective order embedding is an order isomorphism.

A well-order is a total order in which every non-empty subset has minimal element. It is partial if the minimal elements are finite in number.

A lattice is an ordered set in which every finite subset has infimum and infimum and is said to be complete if every subset of it (therefore also the non-finite ones) has infimum and infimum. On a lattice, by defining two binary operations of upper and lower, an algebraic structure is generated.

The well-ordering theorem states that every set can be well-ordered.

Zorn's lemma states that, given a non-empty set in which a partial order relation is defined such that every chain has an upper bound, then such a set contains at least one maximal element. Zorn's lemma implies the well-ordering theorem.

A theory is said to be of the first order if it is possible to express statements and logically deduce theses in a formal way within the set of definition and not in its subsets. On the other hand, those in which one can range even within the subsets are called second-order theories. To formulate a first-order theory, a finite set of symbols, called the alphabet, is needed, a first-order language given by a set of well-formed formulas, a set of logical axioms for logical connectives and quantifiers, a set of proper axioms not deducible from logical ones and a set of inference rules.

A formula that derives from a formal proof is said to be provable. A first-order theory is syntactically complete if every formula is demonstrable or if its negation is, while it is said to be syntactically consistent if there is no formula for which the formula and its negation are demonstrable at the same time.

A first-order language is characterized by an alphabet of symbols, a set of terms, and formulas. The alphabet includes symbols for variables, constants, relations, functions, quantifiers, logical connectives, and punctuation. The terms are the individual constants and the variables. Within a formula it is possible to identify sub-formulas: a variable is called free if it does not appear in any sub-formula, otherwise it is called constrained. A well-formed formula that does not contain free variables is called a closed formula, otherwise it is called an open one. Finally, a first-order language has its own semantics, i.e. a correct formation of sentences such as to be able to create a model for the language.

We define first-order arithmetic language as the first-order language through which it is possible to derive formal theories of arithmetic. The standard model of this language is that of the set of natural numbers with the successor function, defining the symbols of the operations of addition and multiplication and the relation of equality.

A set or property is expressible if there is an open formula that makes it explicit. For example, all recursive sets are expressible.

Given a subset of the set of natural numbers, it is said to be representable if there exists a well-formed formula with a free variable expressing the subset and if, for each natural number belonging to the subset, the formula is provable (or equivalently if for every natural number not belonging to the subset the negation of the formula is demonstrable).

A function is said to be weakly representable if there is a well-formed formula with two free variables that express the function and if, for each pair of natural numbers related to each other through the function, the formula is demonstrable. A function is highly representable if the additional condition given by the fact that the function expressed by the formula also behaves as a function on the natural number also holds.

A first-order theory is Robinson arithmetic denoted by Q whose language is that of first-order arithmetic. The axioms of Q are the logical ones, those of equality are the following proper axioms:

1) 0 is not a successor of any number.
2) Different numbers have different successors, i.e. the successor function is injective.
3) Every number other than 0 is a successor of some other number.
4) Addition can be defined recursively.
5) Multiplication can be defined recursively.

Q is an incomplete theory, in fact it is not possible to deduce the commutative property of addition. Robinson's arithmetic is closely related to that of Peano, denoted by PA. The axioms of PA are the logical ones, those of equality while the proper axioms are those of Robinson with the addition of the principle of induction. With this addition, the commutative property of addition can be deduced. To tell the truth, both arithmetic are based on Peano's axioms which define, at an axiomatic level, the set of natural numbers.

1) There is a natural number 0.
2) Every natural number has a natural successor number.
3) Different numbers have different successors.
4) 0 is not a successor of any natural number.

5) Every subset of natural numbers which contains zero and the successor of each of its elements coincides with the entire set of natural numbers.

These axioms are all independent of each other; the last axiom is that of induction. The triad given by the set of natural numbers, zero and the successor function is characterized by the Peano axioms, up to isomorphisms. Any triad formed by a set, a zero and a function and which satisfies the Peano axioms is called a Peano system. The categoricity theorem states that all Peano systems are isomorphic to the triad given by the set of natural numbers, zero and the successor function.

Peano's axioms are one of the most famous axiomatic systems. An axiomatic system is coherent if it is not possible to derive two contradictory theorems from it, it is independent if each of its axioms is independent and it is complete if it is possible to demonstrate from the axioms the truth or falsehood of each proposition. We shall shortly see the remarkable results of contemporary mathematical logic regarding these properties of axiomatic systems.

An axiomatic system is said to be coherent or consistent if it is impossible to prove a contradiction. Syntactic consistency is such if both a well-formed formula and its negation cannot be proved at the same time. Semantic coherence is such if the theory admits at least one model. For a first order theory the two concepts of coherence just exposed are equivalent.

An axiomatic system is correct if every conclusion is a logical consequence of the axioms.

A first-order axiomatic system is syntactically complete if it is possible to prove or disprove any statement in the language of the system, which means that there is no undecidable statement. A first-order axiomatic system is semantically complete if any formula can be proved to be true in the model. Syntactic completeness is a stronger property than semantic one.

A first-order theory is said to be satisfiable if there is a model that makes all the formulas of the theory true.

The following notable theorems hold:

1) Weak completeness theorem: a theory is satisfiable if and only if the union of the trees of the sequence built starting from the theory is an open tree.

2) Strong completeness theorem: a theory is unsatisfiable if and only if there exists a natural number such that the tree of the sequence is closed.

3) Syntactic compactness theorem: a theory has a closed tree if and only if there is a closed finite subset.

4) Semantic compactness theorem: if every subset of a set of formulas is satisfiable then so is the set. This theorem simplifies for first-order languages: if every finite subset of in a set of formulas has a model then the set has one too.

5) Semidecidability theorem: the union of the trees of the sequence built starting from the theory is a closed tree if and only if there exists a natural number such that the tree of the sequence is closed.

6) Lowenheim-Skolem theorem: if a set of statements has an infinite model then it has a model of any cardinality greater than or equal to the cardinality of the language.

In addition to the classical definition of sets, called naive set theory, it is also possible to define an axiomatic theory of sets. To tell the truth, there are several axiomatic theories of sets that we are now going to explain.

Naive set theory was shelved after the evidence of several paradoxes that will be explained later in this textbook. A first axiomatization was given by Zermelo, but was immediately expanded by Fraenkel to give life to the theory of Zermelo-Fraenkel sets. This theory is based on a first-order language and nine axioms:

1) Extensionality axiom: two sets are equal if and only if they have the same elements.

2) Axiom of the empty set: there exists a set without elements called empty set.

3) Couple axiom: given two sets, then the set that contains only these two sets is a set.

4) Union axiom: every set has a union.

5) Axiom of infinity: there exists a set x such that {} is in x and whenever y is in x, so is the union between y and {y}.

6) Separation axiom: given a set and a generic proposition, there exists a subset that contains the elements for which the proposition holds.

7) Replacement axiom: given a set and an application, there exists a set that contains the images of the elements of the original set according to that application.

8) Power set axiom: for each set x there is a set y such that the elements of y are the subsets of x.
9) Axiom of regularity: every non-empty set contains a given element such that the set and the element are disjoint.

However, some results of logic are not demonstrable only with these nine axioms. A further axiom must be introduced, called the axiom of choice, which gives rise to the axiomatic theory of sets ZFC (where C stands for choice).
The axiom of choice states that, given a non-empty family of non-empty sets, there exists a function which makes one element correspond to each set of the family. The axiom of choice is necessary for the proof that every vector space admits a basis and for the proof of various theorems (that of Hahn-Banach and that of semantic compactness, for example).
It can be seen that the axiom of choice is equivalent to Zorn's lemma, to the well-ordering theorem and to the following Hartogs theorem: given two sets, one always has that the cardinality of one is greater than or equal to or less than or equal to the cardinality of the other so all sets have comparable cardinality even if they are unbounded.
The axiom of countable choice is a weak version of the axiom of choice and states that every countable collection of non-empty sets has a choice function. This axiom is not provable in Zermelo-Fraenkel set theory without introducing the axiom of choice.
From the ZFC axioms all other mathematical concepts are constructed, such as those of number, order, relation and function.
There are some propositions that are independent of ZFC, among these we mention:

1) Cantor's continuum hypothesis: there is no set whose cardinality is strictly between that of integers and that of real numbers.
2) Suslin's hypothesis: given a non-empty totally ordered set such that it has neither maximum nor minimum element, has dense order, is complete and contains a countable dense subset, then there exists an order isomorphism between the set and the real line.

This means that this axiomatic theory cannot be taken as the sole foundation of mathematics, especially after what we will say shortly about Godel's results.

There is instead an undecidable result from Peano's arithmetic but demonstrable in the axiomatic theory of sets and it is Goodstein's theorem.

The base-n inheritance notation (where n is a natural number) is given by the following expression:

$$a_k n^k + a_{k-1} n^{k-1} + \ldots + a_0$$

Where all coefficients a are between 0 and n-1. We define the dilation operation as the substitution of the indices n+1 by those n in a base n+1 inheritance notation. The Goodstein sequence is thus defined by recurrence using the dilation operation (denoted by d):

$$G(1,m) = m$$
$$G(n+1,m) = d(G(n,m)) - 1$$

Goodstein's theorem states that all Goodstein sequences reach zero, whatever the starting value.

A first axiomatic set theory that goes beyond ZFC is the Tarski-Grothendieck theory which is not conservative with respect to ZFC. Many axioms are equivalent to those of ZFC, for example:

1) Ontology: logical quantifiers make sense only on sets.
2) Extensionality axiom: two sets are identical if and only if they have the same elements.
3) Axiom of the empty set: there exists a set of which no other set is an element.
4) Axiom of regularity: no set is an element of itself and circular chains of belonging are not possible.
5) Replacement axiom: the image of a function is a set.

The real novelty is given by Tarski's axiom: for every set x there exists another set y such that x belongs to y, for every z belonging to y then every subset of z is an element of y and the set of parts of z is an element of y, moreover every subset of y whose cardinality is less than that of y is an element of y.

This axiom implies the axioms of the couple, of the power set, of the union, of the infinite and of the choice. This means that the Tarski-Grothendieck axiomatic theory is stronger than the ZFC one.

A conservative extension of ZFC is the axiomatic set theory of Von Neumann-Bernays-Godel which however changes ontology with respect to ZFC.

The fundamental difference from ZFC is the distinction between proper class and set. The belonging of an individual A to another individual B denotes A as a set and B as a class (in this axiomatization sets are denoted by lowercase letters, classes by uppercase ones). It is called universal class V, the class of all sets. The binary relation denoting the set a as representing the class A is called representation. Classes that have no representation are called proper classes.

We can define five axioms about sets (extensionality, coupling, union, power, infinity) in a similar way to what is done by the ZFC scheme; moreover, there are two axioms (extensionality, regularity) defined on classes.

It is typical of this axiomatization to introduce two new axioms about classes:

1) Size limit: for each class C, there exists a set x such that x=C if and only if there is no bijection between C and class V of all sets.

2) Scheme of class comprehension: for every formula not containing quantifiers between classes, there exists a class such that the formula explicits every set belonging to the class.

One of the most advanced results of contemporary mathematical logic is given by the enunciation of Godel's theorems.

Godel's completeness theorem establishes a correspondence between semantic truth and logical provability in first order theories. The theorem states that a deductive system for first-order predicate logic is complete, furthermore all provable formulas are logically valid. From this it follows that a formula is logically valid if and only if it is demonstrable. Generalizing this theorem, it can be said that for every first-order theory and for every closed formula in the first-order language, there exists a formal deduction of the formula starting from the theory if and only if the formula is verified in every model.

A consequence of this theorem is that the logically valid and provable formulas of a theory are a countable quantity.

It should be noted that second-order logics do not have a standard semantic completeness theorem: it is possible to construct correct deductive systems in second-order logic, but such systems are not complete.

Godel has two incompleteness theorems.

XXXII – Advanced mathematical logic

The first states that, in any mathematical theory that contains an arithmetic, there exists a formula such that, if the theory is consistent, then neither the formula nor its negation is provable in the theory. In other words, for any axiomatic theory of natural numbers it is possible to construct a syntactically correct proposition which can neither be proved nor disproved within the theory.

The second theorem states that, in any mathematical theory that contains arithmetic, if the theory is consistent, it is not possible to prove its consistency within the theory. In other words, no coherent system can be used to demonstrate its own coherence.

It is therefore not possible to define the complete list of axioms which allows to demonstrate all truths, as done by Peano for arithmetic or by ZFC for set theory.

Furthermore, it is not possible to solve Hilbert's program ie prove the consistency of all mathematics.

Godel's theorems therefore put very specific limits to mathematical logic and to the very concept of mathematics and science that we have in the contemporary vision.

We call Godel numbering a function which assigns to each production of formal language a single natural number called Godel number.

One of the consequences of Godel's theorems is Tarski's indefinability theorem. Given a language of first-order arithmetic, the theorem states the impossibility of the set of Godel numbers of true statements in the standard structure being defined by a formula of first-order arithmetic. In other words, arithmetic truth cannot be defined within arithmetic itself.

In mathematical logic, paradoxes and antinomies are of particular importance. The paradox is a proposition that is possibly proved and logically coherent, but which goes against common intuition; the antinomy is a real logical contradiction; many times, however, these terms are used interchangeably. There are logical paradoxes of antiquity (for example Zeno's paradox), here we will explain the main paradoxes of modern logic.

Using naïve set theory, Russell's antinomy can be stated: the set of all sets that do not belong to themselves belongs to itself if and only if it does not belong to itself. The logical contradiction of this proposition is evident and yet the statement is formally correct in naive set theory. This antinomy led to the overcoming of the naive theory of sets through axiomatic theories and from here the solution was reached thanks to Godel's incompleteness theorems.

A generalization of Russell's antinomy in linguistic terms is given by the antinomy of heterologicity, also called Grelling-Nelson. This antinomy demonstrates how Russell's antinomy holds for non-mathematical languages as well.

Other reformulations of Russell's antinomy are the paradoxes of the librarian and the barber.

Godel's incompleteness theorem has also given solutions to the so-called semantic paradoxes, such as Richard's and Berry's.

The Burali-Forti antinomy demonstrates how constructing a set of all ordinal numbers leads to a contradiction. This antinomy is overcome in the axiomatic theories of sets by not allowing the existence of a set constructed according to the logical scheme "all sets having a certain property".

The Banach-Tarski paradox, also called paradox of the doubling of the sphere, states that, using the axiom of choice, it is possible to subdivide a sphere in three-dimensional space into a finite and unmeasurable set of pieces, reassembling them by means of rotations and translations in such a way to obtain two spheres of the same radius as the original sphere. In other words, a three-dimensional Euclidean sphere is equidecomposable with two copies of itself.

The finite and non-measurable set is the Vitali set which is invariant under translations and is not measurable in any measure. This set is constructed starting from the interval [0,1] of real numbers and defining, within it, an equivalence relation if the difference between two numbers is a rational number; the set of all equivalence classes of this relation consists of an uncountable infinity. Then the axiom of choice states that there exists a set which contains a representative of each class and this set is the Vitali set.

There are other types of logic than what has been presented so far.

Natural deduction represents and codifies a deductive system, therefore without axioms and with a series of inference rules dependent on primitive connectives. It should be noted that, in the face of Godel's incompleteness theorems for axiomatic systems, deductive systems are the correct basis for mathematical proof and for scientific knowledge. An inference rule can be introduced or eliminated for each logical constant and is divided into two parts: the premises or hypotheses, which are placed before the rule itself, and the conclusions or theses, which are placed after it. Natural deduction is the basis of both minimal and intuitionistic logic, while the main assumptions are those of the principles of identity and the excluded middle, already introduced in elementary logic.

Intuitionistic logic is also called constructive logic and assumes that every statement must be demonstrated to be considered true. For example, the principle of the excluded middle is not considered valid in this logic because it is not justifiable and therefore intuitionistic logic is not based on the concept of truth, but on that of justifiability. In this logic, a correct demonstration is not the one which preserves the validity from the hypotheses to the thesis, but it is the one which preserves its justifiability. Another example of a classical tautology rejected by this logic is that of the double negative. This logic finds ample space and great applications in computer programming.

Modal logic expresses how a proposition can be true or false. The basic modal operators are the one expressing necessity, denoted by a square, and the one expressing possibility, denoted by a diamond. The two operators are linked together by the double negation: applying the operator of necessity (or probability) to a proposition is equivalent to applying the negation of the operator possibility (or necessity) on the negation of the proposition. The aletic modalities are those connected to the truthfulness mode of a statement and are divided into logical possibility, physical possibility and metaphysical possibility. There are also epistemic modalities characterized by the knowledge and belief modal operators, denoted by the capital letters K and C. The belief operator satisfies some basic principles, including that of introspection, that of epistemic non-contradiction, that of non-implication of truth and that of the impossibility of the non-certainty of doubt. The operator of knowledge, in turn, satisfies the principle of implication of truth, of implication of belief, of epistemic non-contradiction and of introspection. There are also time and duty modes to characterize such operators based on time and the concept of leave. It is also possible to axiomatize a modal logic, for example Kripke's logic foresees all the axioms of the first order logic with in addition an axiom concerning the necessity and one concerning the distribution of the modal operator necessity. Other modal logics also use the transitive, symmetric, serial, and Euclidean properties. In modal logic, Barcan's formula (with its inverse) represents a relationship between quantifiers and modal operators: the operator of necessity can be exchanged with the quantifier it defines "for each" and vice versa.

Dynamic logic is an extension of modal logic and in fact is also referred to as multimodal. The necessity and possibility operators are generalized to a number of propositions and not to a single statement. The axiomatizations of this logic are very similar to those of modal logic, also managing to derive compound inference rules and to axiomatize the classic visions of modus ponens and modus tollens. Particularly important in this logic is the statement of assignment which, starting from a scheme of axioms, allows the construction of arithmetic and elementary algebra operations. Furthermore, in dynamic logic, each proposition is associated with an action called test which allows to derive the normal laws of logical implication and to reduce the quantification operator to the concept of causal assignment. First-order logic derives from dynamic logic by simply assigning to an action the value of the test on the single proposition. Dynamic logic applied to normal first-order logic is called propositional dynamic logic and allows a great leap forward, above all to bring the field of logic to the application level of artificial intelligence.

Descriptive logics represent a family of formalisms which, through relevant concepts in the domain of application, specify the properties of objects and individuals belonging to this domain, called the world. These logics, starting from an ontology, use a representation of knowledge through the so-called reasoner, obtaining explicit concepts from the ontology itself. There are various descriptive logics, in particular they make use of the possibility of using the negation operator, the possibility of defining hierarchies, the possibility of enumerating objects and individuals, the possibility of introducing the inverse role of operators, the possibility of introducing conjunction operators, quantifiers and cardinalities.

The generic logics in standard T are logics characterized by an application T defined in [0,1] x [0,1], which sends values in [0,1], having the commutative, associative, monotonicity and endowed properties of null element and of the identity one. In this logic it is possible to define the connectives of conjunction and disjunction on the basis of the T norm.

Polyvalent logics are extensions of classical logic in which the principle of the excluded middle does not apply as there are more truth values than the classical true and false. For example, a multipurpose logic proposed by Post was a logic with three truth values: true, false and problematic. There are also logics with infinite truth values, such as Godel's multipurpose logic:

$$x \wedge y = \min(v(x), v(y))$$
$$x \vee y = \max(v(x), v(y))$$
$$\bar{x} = 1 \Leftrightarrow v(x) = 0$$
$$\bar{x} = 0 \Leftrightarrow v(x) \neq 0$$

Or the multipurpose product logic:

$$x \wedge y = v(x)v(y)$$
$$x \vee y = v(x) + v(y) - v(x)v(y)$$
$$\bar{x} = 1 \Leftrightarrow v(x) = 0$$
$$\bar{x} = 0 \Leftrightarrow v(x) \neq 0$$

In these logics, the double negative is not valid. These logics are extensions of the Boolean one.

Among the multipurpose logics, fuzzy logics have a primary importance, i.e. logics whose degree of truth of a proposition can be between 0 and 1. These logics base their foundations on the definition of fuzzy sets and are fundamental for modern evolutions of finance, statistics, neural networks, chaos theory, numerical and electronic calculation as well as in the vast majority of scientific applications.

Fuzzy set theory is an extension of classical set theory in which the principles of non-contradiction and the excluded middle are not valid, substantially rejecting, like all polyvalent logics, the bivalence of truth and the semantic paradoxes generated over the centuries, as the classic example of establishing the veracity of the following proposition "this sentence is false". In a fuzzy logic the truth values are defined according to the Zadeh operators:

$$x \wedge y = \min(v(x), v(y))$$
$$x \vee y = \max(v(x), v(y))$$
$$\bar{x} = 1 - v(x)$$

XXXII – Advanced mathematical logic

Note

APOSTILLA

As it has been noted in the development of all the topics, mathematics has in itself an almost unlimited breadth of sectors and applications. There is no science that can do without mathematical concepts and there is no application that has not borrowed mathematical notions and made them evolve with particular languages.

This is how many disciplines and many theories not presented in this manual were born, citing just a few examples we can include game theory and financial mathematics in the economic field, the applications of group theory and advanced algebra for theoretical physics and elementary particles, the evolution of tensor calculus for problems in cosmology and astrophysics.

The evolution of mathematics applied to individual disciplines and technologies has led to extreme ramifications and continuous evolution that continues even today.

This has an important consequence: mathematics is a "living", contemporary and future science and is not relegated to a historical role. What has been said does not apply only to the countless applications, but also to "pure" mathematics, i.e. to the mathematical problems presented in this manual.

By making a historicism about the notions and results expressed in this paper, one could clearly see how some assumptions and some demonstrations are very recent (an example above all is the demonstration of the Poincaré conjecture) that is, they took place in the Twenty-First Century. It is no coincidence that there are prizes for solving problems that are still open and that are both historic, such as Hilbert's famous questions from the early twentieth century, and very modern in relation to computational calculation, logic, complexity and chaos theory, as well as geometric and algebraic concepts.

Being a living science, just like a universal language, mathematics is continuously enriched with new words and new constructs and that is why what is presented in this book is only a stepping stone towards even more advanced and specific knowledge.

Taking up the challenge of writing a new chapter or a single chapter in this compelling story of the only universal artificial language that

295

Note

describes Nature is part of the evolution of our species and that is why each of us is called to participate in it.

Printed in the USA
CPSIA information can be obtained
at www.ICGtesting.com
LVHW011640010823
754086LV00045B/1071